the AMAZING SPIDER-MAN

THE MENACE OF MYSTERIO!

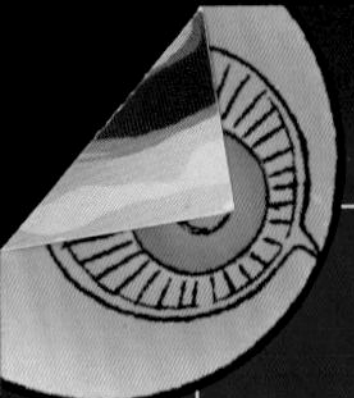

FRIENDLY NEIGHBORHOOD SPIDER-MAN #11-13

Peter David
Writer

Todd Nauck
Pencils

Robert Campanella & Rodney Ramos (#11)
Inks

Lee Loughridge
Colours

VC's Cory Petit
Letters

Mike Wieringo, Mike Manley & Paul Mounts
Cover Art

Michael O'Connor
Assistant Editor

Axel Alonso
Editor

Joe Quesada
Editor in Chief

THE AMAZING SPIDER-MAN #618-620

Dan Slott
Writer

Marcos Martin & Javier Pulido (#620)
Art

Javier Rodriguez
Colours

VC's Joe Caramagna
Letters

Tom Brennan
Assistant Editor

Stephen Wacker
Editor

Tom Brevoort
Executive Editor

Joe Quesada
Editor in Chief

THE AMAZING SPIDER-MAN #13

Stan Lee
Writer

Steve Ditko
Art

Art Simek
Letters

Glynis Oliver-Wein
Colours

the AMAZING SPIDER-MAN

When Stan Lee and Steve Ditko created Spider-Man, they didn't just invent an iconic hero – they created a whole host of iconic foes for him too! From the Green Goblin to Doctor Octopus, Spidey was gifted a seminal set of super villains who were unparalleled in their inventiveness. In this book we shine a light on one of the web-head's most innovative antagonists, a charlatan whose tricks are as deadly as they are ingenious, a performer whose repertoire is guaranteed to slay any audience, the master of mystery and magic... Mysterio!

We begin with a tale from 2006 written by Peter David, with art by Todd Nauck. Taking place just after Spider-Man had revealed his civilian identity to the world at large in *Civil War*, this tale sees Mysterio – or at least a version of him – take his revenge on Peter Parker. Part super-hero story, part haunted-house tale, this is an action-packed and unpredictable adventure filled with unexpected events that keeps everyone on their toes – including the villains!

Next up, we jump to 2010 for a tale of murder, mystery and mobsters as the super villain takes advantage of the current underworld chaos in New York City. Written by Spidey-scribe extraordinaire Dan Slott, with art by the immeasurably talented Marcos Martin, we see Mysterio mess with Spider-Man's head once again in an attempt to push him to breaking point. As with all the best Mysterio tales, this is one where once again, nothing is really quite what it seems.

Finally, we present the insane illusionist's debut from *Amazing Spider-Man #13* by the legendary Stan Lee and Steve Ditko. A perfect example of the pair's pioneering efforts to inject soap-opera storytelling into comics and create more believable characters (while still providing a visual treat for readers that no other publisher could match), this is without doubt a classic slice of swinging 60s Spider-Man!

So read on! The Master of Illusion awaits...

Ed Hammond
Marvel Editor, Panini UK

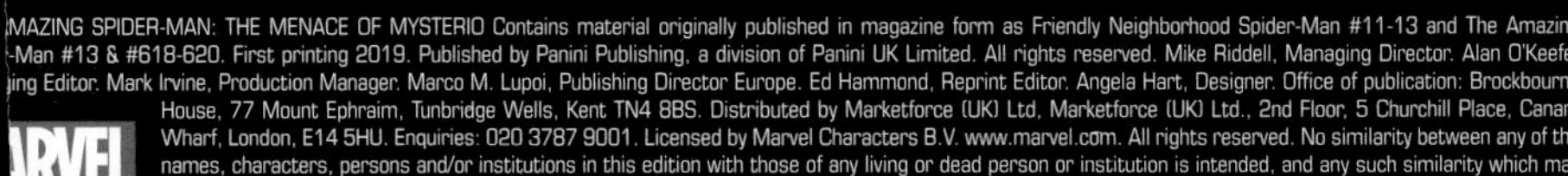

MAZING SPIDER-MAN: THE MENACE OF MYSTERIO Contains material originally published in magazine form as Friendly Neighborhood Spider-Man #11-13 and The Amazing -Man #13 & #618-620. First printing 2019. Published by Panini Publishing, a division of Panini UK Limited. All rights reserved. Mike Riddell, Managing Director. Alan O'Keefe, ing Editor. Mark Irvine, Production Manager. Marco M. Lupoi, Publishing Director Europe. Ed Hammond, Reprint Editor. Angela Hart, Designer. Office of publication: Brockbourne House, 77 Mount Ephraim, Tunbridge Wells, Kent TN4 8BS. Distributed by Marketforce (UK) Ltd, Marketforce (UK) Ltd., 2nd Floor, 5 Churchill Place, Canary Wharf, London, E14 5HU. Enquiries: 020 3787 9001. Licensed by Marvel Characters B.V. www.marvel.com. Printed in the United Kingdom by Zenith Media. ISBN: 978-1-84653-258-0

THE STORY SO FAR...

Life has changed a lot for Peter Parker in the last few months. He is now a member of the Avengers and has moved into Avengers Tower along with his wife Mary Jane and Aunt May.

In his civilian life, Peter has just started a new job – science teacher at his old high school Midtown High. Though Peter enjoys teaching, he's certainly feeling a sense of déjà vu, especially as his former tormentor Flash Thompson also works there as the gym teacher.

Since joining the Avengers, Spider-Man has developed a much closer friendship with billionaire inventor Tony Stark, AKA Iron Man. Following a near-death encounter with a creature called Morlun, Tony built Spider-Man a new hi-tech suit to help protect him. Along with a multi-functional armoured skin, communication arrays, enhanced vision, filters and glider wings, it also features three extra retractable mechanical arms.

Recently, the super-hero community has been split in two by the introduction of the Superhuman Registration Act which demands that all super-powered individuals must be registered with the government. Tony Stark has become the figurehead of the pro-SHRA side, while Captain America has refused to accept the law and now leads a band of underground heroes.

In order to help encourage support for the act, Spider-Man agreed to unmask on national television, revealing to the world that he was Peter Parker.

FRIENDLY NEIGHBORHOOD SPIDER-MAN #11

IT'S ALMOST TOO EASY.
THE ONE DIFFICULTY WAS GOING TO BE CHASING AROUND THE CITY, FINDING HIM. BUT NOOOO. HE HAD TO GO TAKE CARE OF THAT.
"HELLO, EVERYONE. I'M PETER PARKER. I TEACH AT A SCHOOL IN NEW YORK.
"INSTEAD OF WEARING A BIG SPIDER ON MY BACK...
"...I'VE DECIDED TO PAINT THIS BIG HONKIN' TARGET. I HOPE THAT'S OKAY WITH ALL OF YOU."
FUNNY YOU SHOULD ASK.

BECAUSE IT'S PERFECTLY FINE WITH ME.
YOU WANT TO MAKE IT THAT MUCH EASIER FOR ME TO AVENGE WHAT YOU DID TO MY BROTHER? THAT'S YOUR LOOKOUT!
THE ORIGINAL MYSTERIO MAY HAVE BEEN ALL ABOUT TRICKS AND SPECIAL EFFECTS.
BUT NOW YOU'RE DEALING WITH FRANCIS KLUM, AND MY POWERS OF TELEPORTATION WILL--
--EASILY PROVE TO BE FAR MORE THAN ANYTH...
YAK, YAK, YAK. HE CERTAINLY DOES LOVE THE SOUND OF HIS OWN VOICE. LUCKY I HAVE A VOLUME CONTROL.
SPIDER-MAN WILL BE FORTUNATE IF THIS OAF DOESN'T TALK HIM TO DEATH.

SPIDERS
S.O.S. SHOVE OFF SPIDER-MAN
YOU'RE GOING TO GET OUR CHILDREN KILLED!
JAMESON'S BEEN RIGHT ABOUT YOU FOR YEARS! YOU DON'T CARE ABOUT ANYTHING EXCEPT YOURSELF!
OUR CHILDREN ARE AT RISK
GO TEACH IN LONG ISLAND! YOU CAN BE THEIR PROBLEM!
WHAT DO YOU SAY TO PARENTS WHO ARE AFRAID MORE SUPER-VILLAINS WILL ATTACK YOU AND ENDANGER THEIR CHILDREN?!
BOXERS OR BRIEFS, SIR?
KEEP AWAY FROM OUR KIDS!
IS IT TRUE YOU'VE BEEN ASKED FOR YO RESIGNATION
DOES YOUR NOW MOSTLY-RED COSTUME INDICATE YOU'VE GIVEN UP "BLUE STATE" LIBERAL THINKING?
WE'D JUST LIKE YOU TO TALK TO US FOR A FEW MINUTES, PETER!

OH-KAY. THAT'S ENOUGH OF THAT.
WHOA!
AMAZING!
SPECTACULAR!
SENSATIONAL!
NOT ESPECIALLY FRIENDLY, THOUGH.

THIS IS INSANE. I CAN'T KEEP OPERATING LIKE THIS.
ANYTIME I SET FOOT OUTSIDE OF STARK TOWERS, THE PRESS AND PROTESTORS ARE WAITING FOR ME.

ROOFTOP ACCESS
TONY KEEPS SWEARING IT'S GONNA DIE DOWN, BUT I DUNNO... IT JUST SEEMS TO BE GETTING BIGGER AND BIGGER.
POOR MJ AND AUNT MAY ARE PRACTICALLY PRISONERS OF AVENGERS HQ NOW. I'M STARTING TO THINK THIS WAS THE BIGGEST MISTAKE OF MY LIFE.

HEY, MR. PARKER.
HEY BACK AT YOU, JERE--
PERSONNEL ONLY
FIRE

JEREMY!
WHAT THE HEL--
--HECK HAPPENED TO YOU?

WAS BRAD GIVING YOU GRIEF AGAIN?
NAH. HAPPENED IN GYM. DODGEBALL. THE NEW NURSE PUT SOME ICE ON IT, SAID IT'LL BE OKAY.
DODGE-BALL?
SURE. YOU MUSTA HAD IT EVEN WHEN YOU WERE A KID, RIGHT?
OHHHHH YEAH. BACK THEN, WHEN DINOSAURS ROAMED THE EARTH, WE STILL HAD DODGE-BALL.
MR. PARKER, YOU'RE A SCIENCE TEACHER. YOU KNOW DINOSAURS DIED MILLIONS OF--
FIGURE OF SPEECH, JEREMY. I'LL SEE YOU LATER.
YEAH, HAD A FEELING I'D SEE YOU SOONER OR LATER, PARKER. WHAT, LITTLE JEREMY CAME WHINING TO YOU?
AND YOU FIGURED...WHAT? THAT I'D BE ALL INTIMIDATED...?
BECAUSE I'D BE DUMB ENOUGH TO BUY INTO THIS WHOLE "PETER PARKER IS SPIDER-MAN" SCAM?
"SCAM?" FLASH, YOU CAN'T STILL THINK IT'S...
I'LL GIVE YOU PROPS FOR HELPING SPIDEY OUT. IT'S A BRILLIANT DODGE. GET THOSE GOVERNMENT JERKS OFF HIS TAIL.
BUT I KNOW THE DEAL ONCE THIS LAW TH BLOWS OVER, YO AND SPIDEY'LL B SEEN TOGETHER A THAT'LL BE THAT

EXIT
FINE, FLASH. WHATEVER. LOOK, LAST TIME YOU GOT HUFFY WHEN I WENT TO THE PRINCIPAL, SO THIS TIME I'M COMING STRAIGHT TO YOU.
RATCHET DOWN THE VIOLENCE LEVEL IN DODGEBALL, OKAY? THAT'S ALL I'M ASKING.

IT'S A GAME, PARKER, THAT'S ALL. A HARMLESS GAME. NO ONE EXCEPT A WIMP EVER GOT HIMSELF HURT PLAYING DODGE-BALL.
BUT THEN, 'OU'D KNOW ALL *ABOUT* THAT, WOULDN'T YOU?
COACH

FLASH... YOU'RE LUCKY THAT *ONE* OF US REMEMBERS WE WERE FRIENDS.
LOOK, THERE'S A LOT ON MY MIND RIGHT NOW, SO JUST--

WHAT'S THE *MATTER*, PETEY?
C'MON. LESSEE WHAT YOU'VE GOT.
OH, GROW UP, WOULD YOU, PLEA--

AREN'T YOU THE TYPE WHO ALWAYS TELLS KIDS THEY SHOULD STAND UP TO BULLIES?
AFRAID TO *PRACTICE* WHAT YOU *PREACH?* TO TAKE SOME RESPONSIBILITY FOR WHAT YOU'RE TELLING THE STUDENTS?
COACH

SIGH
FINE. LET'S GO.

C'MON, PARKER! YOU GET FIRST SHOT! GIVE IT YOUR BEST!
COACH
SIGH
LAST CHANCE TO BACK OUT OF THIS, FLASH.
OH YEAH! YEAH, THAT'S A SPECTACULAR SPIDER-THROW ALRIGHT!
COACH
HERE! LEMME SHOW YOU HOW IT'S DONE!
JUST LIKE THE OLD DAYS!
RIGHT. JUST LIKE.

WAKKK
EXIT
WAM

COACH?
COACH, CAN YOU HEAR ME?
HERE, LET ME TRY SMELLING SALTS.

YES. *THAT'S* BRINGING HIM AROUND.
COACH...CAN YOU TELL ME YOUR NAME?
The teacher didn't say there was gonna be a quiz.

OKAY, YOUR FIRST NAME IS "FLASH." DO YOU KNOW YOUR LAST NAME?
Gordon?

OH, LORD. WE'RE GOING TO GET SUED OVER THIS...
RELAX, ROGER.
MY FACE KINDA HURTS, BUT OTHER THAN THAT, I'M FINE. AND *HELLOOOOOO*, NURSE. YOU ARE...?
THIS IS MISS ARROW, THE NEW SCHOOL NURSE.
LET'S TAKE YOU BACK TO THE OFFICE AND PUT SOME ICE ON THOSE.
"THOSE?"
THOSE *WHAT?*

WHAT? ARE YOU KIDDING ME?
YOU GOT SENT TO THE PRINCIPAL'S OFFICE? WHAT FOR?
DODGEBALL? PETER, YOU CAN'T BE SERI--
OFF HIS *FACE?* THAT WAS DUMB!
WHAT HAPPENED, DEAR?
PETER BOUNCED A DODGEBALL OFF ANOTHER TEACHER'S FACE AND BROKE HIS NOSE.
FOR HEAVEN'S SAKE. HE SHOULD KNOW BETTER THAN THAT! OF ALL THE--
IT WAS FLASH THOMPSON.
AH. THE ONE WHO USED TO BE HIS FRIEND BUT IS NOW BACK TO BEING LIKE HE WAS IN HIGH SCHOOL.
RIGHT.
WELL...HE PROBABLY HAD IT COMING, THEN.

WHAT DID AUNT MAY SAY?
SHE AGREED WITH ME AND SAID IT WAS DUMB.
WHY DO I NOT BELIEVE YOU?
BECAUSE YOU'RE A MEAN, TERRIBLE HUSBAND WHO HAS NO REASON NOT TO TRUST ME.
HOW ABOUT THAT YOU LIE?
BESIDE THAT.

MJ, SERIOUSLY...I THINK I MAY HAVE TO BAG THIS TEACHING GIG.
THE PRESS IS CAMPED OUTSIDE, THE PARENTS ARE COMPLAINING...
AND THE KIDS KEEP STARING AT ME LIKE THAT TRICYCLE KID IN "THE INCREDIBLES," WAITING FOR ME TO DO "SOMETHING AMAZING."
IT KILLS ME, BUT--
GOTTA GO.

DID I HEAR YOU SAY SOME-THING'S OUT TO KILL YOU, PETER?
NOT LITERALLY, SIR.
AH, WELL...

WHAT A NICE CHANGE OF PACE.
PLEASE, SIT. SIT.

SO! WE HAVE A BIT OF A SITUATION ON OUR HANDS, DON'T WE?
ROGER, IF YOU NEED ME TO APOLOGIZE TO FLASH--
ONLY IF YOUR CONSCIENCE COMPELS YOU TO, PETER. FROM WHAT I HEAR, HE PROVOKED YOU INTO IT. YOU ASK ME, HE GOT WHAT HE ASKED FOR, CHALLENGING SPIDER-MAN...

BUT IT'S THE "*SPIDER-MAN THING*" THAT'S THE PROBLEM, ISN'T IT?
IT IS SOMEWHAT, YES. I WON'T LIE TO YOU.
HERE'S WHERE WE STAND, PETER...

THE FACT IS, PARENTS ARE PUTTING PRESSURE ON ME TO GET RID OF YOU.
BUT, BETWEEN YOU, ME AND THE LAMPPOST, I'VE ALWAYS BEEN A HUGE FAN OF YOUR...ALTER EGO.
I'M DISINCLINED TO PENALIZE YOU SIMPLY BECAUSE YOU'VE SPENT YOUR LIFE RISKING YOUR NECK WHILE ***HELPING*** PEOPLE.

AND WHEN THE TIME CAME TO DO EVEN MORE...TO OBEY THE LAW...YOU DID SO.
SO I WANT YOU TO KNOW THAT I'VE GOT YOUR BACK. NO MATTER HOW MUCH PARENTS COMPLAIN, NO MATTER HOW MUCH PRESSURE, I'M NOT GOING TO DEMAND--

ROGER, I'VE DECIDED TO RESIGN.

OH, THANK ***GOD.***

I MEAN...ARE YOU ***SURE*** YOU WON'T RECONSIDER?
I'D LIKE TO FINISH OUT THE DAY, IF THAT'S ALL RIGHT. I'M THE ADVISOR FOR THE ECOLOGY CLUB, AND I DON'T WANT TO LEAVE THEM IN THE LURCH.
YES, YES, BY ***ALL*** MEANS. AND PETER...
IF YOU CHANGE YOUR MIND...I MEANT EVERYTHING I SAID.
I APPRECIATE THAT. AND I DON'T KNOW WHAT ELSE TO SAY, EXCEPT--

THIS SUCKS.
GLOBAL WARMING PROJECT
JEREMY? WHAT DID--?
THAT YOU'RE LEAVING. IT SUCKS.
YEAH.
LOOK, GUYS...
WHY SHOULD WE BOTHER STARTING THIS STUPID PROJECT ABOUT GLOBAL WARMING IF YOU WON'T BE AROUND TO SEE IT FINISHED?
BECAUSE IT'S IMPORTANT.
SO IS YOUR TEACHING HERE, AND YOU'RE DUMPING US.
I'M NOT "DUMPING" YOU. IT'S...LOOK, IT'S COMPLICATED.
BUT THERE'S PLENTY OF GOOD TEACHERS OUT THERE--
IF YOU BELIEVED THAT, YOU WOULDN'T HAVE COME HERE IN THE FIRST PLACE.
THAT'S NOT--
WAIT A MINUTE.
WHAT IS IT?
SOMETHING'S...

SO THAT'S YOUR WHOLE NAME? ARROW?
WHAT CAN I TELL YOU? MY PARENTS WERE INVETERATE HIPPIES.
I THINK IT'S AN INTERESTING NAME.
"INTERESTING." THAT'S NONCOMMITTAL.
YEAH, WELL, I'VE GOT COMMITMENT ISSUES.
FUNNY MAN. HERE I THOUGHT YOU WERE AN EMPTY-HEADED JOCK-TYPE.
OH, I GOT LAYERS.
REALLY.
DEFINITELY. YOU, UH...
YOU INTO LAYERS?
UNLESS YOU, Y'KNOW...GOT PROBLEMS WITH THE WHOLE BLACK/WHITE THING.
THE WORLD'S NOT BLACK-AND-WHITE, COACH. JUST SHADES OF GRAY.
TRUE ENOUGH. AND, HEY...CALL ME--
CRIPES!
"CRIPES?" THAT'S AN UNUSUAL...
OH.
COACH

SPIDER MAN UNSAFE FOR OUR KIDS
SPIDERMAN DON'T TEACH
LIVE! GO LIVE!
I DON'T CARE IF THE VIEW IS ON! BREAK IN, RIGHT NOW!
MY KID IS STILL IN THERE!
NO SPIDER
GET THEM BACK! GET THESE PEOPLE BACK! NOW!
SPIDER MAN GO HOME
NYPD
THIS IS JO NADY REPORTING. A MYSTERIOUS CLOUD OF ABSOLUTE BLACKNESS HAS ENVELOPED THE PUBLIC SCHOOL WHERE PETER PARKER, THE RECENTLY REVEALED SPIDER-MAN, REMAINS A CONTROVERSIAL TEACHER.
ALTHOUGH IT'S AFTER-HOURS, STAFF AND A HANDFUL OF STUDENTS REMAIN INSIDE. IT IS UNCERTAIN AT THIS TIME WHAT NEGATIVE PROPERTIES THIS CLOUD MAY--
UNH...
WUMF

ATTENTION, BOYS AND GIRLS... WE HAVE A SPECIAL ANNOUNCEMENT.
ARROW

YOUR SCHOOL IS NOW...OH, WHAT'S THE BEST WAY TO PUT IT?
"HAUNTED." YES. THAT'S THE WORD.

YOU'RE NOW IN A BIG OLD HAUNTED HOUSE, WHERE GHOSTS AND GOBLINS HOLD SWAY...
AND JUST ABOUT ANYTHING CAN HAPPEN.
SPOOKY STUFF, KIDS.

THE ECK WITH THAT!
OH, AND BEFORE ANY CLEVER PERSON THINKS HE CAN ESCAPE OUT A WINDOW...
BE AWARE THEY'RE ALL WIRED TO A FAIRLY LARGE BOMB THAT WILL BLOW YOU ALL INTO THE STRATOSPHERE. OPEN A WINDOW, AND--

BOOM.
THE FRONT DOOR IS YOUR ONLY WAY OUT. GOOD LUCK.
WHAT'RE WE GONNA DO?!?

I'LL TELL YOU WHAT WE'RE GONNA DO...

WE'RE GONNA GET OUT OF HERE.
STAY CLOSE TO ME AND YOU'LL BE FINE.
THE LIGHTS!
DON'T WORRY. HE'S JUST TRYING TO SPOOK YOU.
WELL, HE'S DOIN' A BANG-UP JOB!

WHO'S *DOING* THIS, MR. PARKER?!?
DOPE! HE'S NOT *MR. PARKER* NOW! YOU GOTTA CALL HIM *SPIDER-MAN!* OR SPIDEY! OR YOUR NEIGHBORLY FRIENDLY SPIDER-MAN.
THAT'S FRIENDLY NEIGHBORHOOD SPIDER-MAN, AND I'M NOT SURE WHO'S DOING IT.
THE *VOICE* SOUNDS FAMILIAR, BUT IT'S FILTERED THROUGH SOME SORT OF ELECTRONIC DEVICE.
NOW, LOOK... IT'S PROBABLY BEST IF WE KEEP THE CHATTER DOWN, OKAY?
GOOD.
DON'T WORRY. I'VE BEEN IN TONS OF SITUATIONS LIKE THIS. JUST TRUST ME.
YOU *DO* TRUST ME, RIGHT?
GUYS, IT'S *OKAY* TO TALK IF I ASK YOU A--
AW, *CRAP.*
GUYS? GUYS?

SPIDEY? THIS ISN'T THE WAY TOWARD THE FRONT ENTRANCE.
YEAH. IS THIS SOME SORT OF TRICK TO FOOL THE--
AAAAHHHH!!!
BOO.
AAAHHH!!
AAAAAAHHHH!!!
CALM DOWN! CALM DOWN, FOR CRYIN' OUT LOUD!
IT'S US!
THERE'S A GUY! A WEIRD GUY!
WHERE?
HE WAS RIGHT THERE!

AUDITORIUM
THIS IS BEAUTIFUL.
IT'S GOING EXACTLY AS I PLANNED. I'VE RIGGED UP THE *ENTIRE SCHOOL* WITH HAUNTINGS AND DEATH TRAPS.
THE HOLOPROJECTION OF SPIDER-MAN SENT THE CHILDREN OFF INTO A COMPLETELY DIFFERENT DIRECTION. EVERYONE'S ROAMING AROUND IN THE DARKNESS...
AND THE BEST THING OF ALL IS THAT NONE OF THEM REALIZES MY TRUE PLAN, OR--
WHA--? WHERE'S *THAT* COMING FROM?
DO YOU HAVE ANY IDEA HOW SICK I AM OF LISTENING TO YOU DECLAIMING TO YOURSELF?
IT'S EMBARRASSING. I SWEAR, I DON'T NOW WHAT'S GOTTEN NTO YOUNG PEOPLE THESE DAYS.
IT... *NO*. IT...
TO BE MEMORABLE, YOU NEED MORE THAN EGOTISTIC RANTING! YOU NEED STYLE! PANACHE! AND MOST OF ALL--

--TIMING.
THAT IS...IF YOU HAVE ANY HOPE OF PRESENTING YOURSELF AS MY SUCCESSOR.

FRIENDLY NEIGHBORHOOD SPIDER-MAN #12

COVER ARTWORK

WILL YOU KEEP THESE PEOPLE BACK, TERELLI?
OKAY, EVERYONE BACK, BACK AWAY FROM THE BARRICADES, PLEASE!
CAPTAIN, CAN I SHOOT A FEW OF THEM JUST TO GET THE POINT ACROSS?
NO.
AT LEAST THREATEN TO?
NO.
OKAY, SIR, BUT YOU'RE JUST MAKING THIS TAKE LONGER.
LOOKS LIKE I PICKED THE WRONG WEEK TO GIVE UP SMOKING.
WHO THE HELL IS IN THERE, ANYWAY?
HIS NAME IS FRANCIS KLUM. BUT HE LIKES TO PRETEND HE'S MYSTERIO.
OH, YEAH? AND HOW DO YOU KNOW--
HOLY--!!!

THE REASON I KNOW THIS SHOULD BE *READILY* APPARENT.
I WAS WATCHING THIS FIASCO ON THE NEWS AND IMMEDIATELY RECOGNIZED THE TYPE OF SMOKE BEING USED. ONE OF MY SIMPLER TRICKS, REALLY.
SO I DECIDED TO SWING BY AND LEND A HAND.
OUT OF
SCHOOL
PETER PARKER

"LEND A HAND?"
LAST I CHECKED, YOU WERE ONE OF THE BAD GUYS.
GO AWAY SPIDERMAN
CAPTAIN, CAPTAIN...HAVE YOU NEVER HEARD OF THE ART OF WAR?
I DON'T GET OUT TO THE MOVIES MUCH.
"THE ENEMY OF MY ENEMY IS MY FRIEND."
NONE OF YOUR PEOPLE CAN PENETRATE THAT CLOUD. MY HELMET, HOWEVER, WILL PROTECT ME.
WISH ME LUCK, "FRIEND."
WE'RE JUST LETTING HIM GO, CAPTAIN?
I'M NOT ENTIRELY SURE WE COULD'VE STOPPED HIM.
BESIDES, MAYBE WE'LL BE LUCKY. THEY'LL WIND UP KILLING EACH OTHE AND OUR PROBLEM WILL BE SOLVED.

KIDS! KIIIIIIDS!!!
NUTS! THEY E RIGHT BEHIND A SECOND AGO! WHERE DID--
UH-OH. THAT DOESN'T LOOK GOOD.
FORTUNATELY ENOUGH, THE COSTUME HAS AN ONBOARD OXYGEN SUPPLY AND FILTRATION SYSTEM.
SO I DON'T HAVE TO WORRY ABOUT INHALING WHATEVER'S IN THAT STUFF AND GOING NUTS OVER IT.
WAIT A MINUTE. HE DOESN'T KNOW THAT.
MIGHT BE A WAY TO LURE HIM OUT.
ARRRRRHHHH!!!
NO! GET AWAY!!!!

MONSTERS! MONSTERS EVERYWHERE!!!
TOO MANY OF THEM! I CAN'T FIGHT THEM--!
NOOOO! NOOOOOO!!!

THE HORROR! THE HORROR! I--

PETER? YOU OKAY?
HUH?

OH. ROGER. HEY. YOU'RE HERE TOO, HUH?
WELL, I AM THE PRINCIPAL, PETER, SO I'M USUALLY THE LAST ONE OUT OF THE BUILDING.
WHAT WAS ALL THAT JUST NOW?

I WAS, UH... TRYING TO ACT SCARED. TO, UH, TO LURE OUT THE BAD GUYS.
NOT CONVINCING, HUH?
LET'S JUST SAY THAT, AS A THESPIAN, YOU'RE A GREAT SCIENCE TEACHER.
YEAH, WELL, YOU WANT ACTING, GO GET TOBEY MAGUIRE.

DOWN!!!

IS THAT-- ARE THOSE BATS?!?!
LOOKS LIKE.
I HATE BATS!
EVERYBODY DOES.
HUH. MAYBE I SHOULD'VE DRESSED UP LIKE A BAT INSTEAD OF A SPIDER. STRIKE FEAR INTO MY ENEMIES...
NAH. DUMB IDEA.
PETER---!!!!

PETEEEEERRRR!!!
MARY JANE!!!
MARY JANE!!!
THEY'VE GOT MY WIFE!
H-HOW DO YOU KNOW WHAT WE JUST SAW WAS REAL?
I DON'T! BUT I CAN'T TAKE THE CHANCE!
WAIT HERE!
HERE? MYSE
SCREW THAT!
PETER! WAIT FO ME!!
"WHO ARE YOU SUPPOSED TO BE?"

YOU NEED TO ASK?
AUDITORIUM
I KNOW WHO YOU'RE PRETENDING TO BE.
NO "PRETENDING" NECESSARY. I'M THE MAN WHOSE CLOTHES YOU'RE WEARING.
GOOD LORD. DID MY THIGHS REALLY LOOK THAT BIG IN THEM?
FWOOOF
ARRRHHH!!!

SON OF A--!
NOW, NOW-- LANGUAGE. WE'RE IN A SCHOOL, REMEMBER. HAVE TO BE WARY OF YOUNGSTERS' INNOCENT EARS.
IT WAS A CUTE TRICK, THOUGH. USING YOUR NATURAL ABILITY AS A TELEPORTER TO TRY AND MATERIALIZE WHERE I WAS STANDING. BASICALLY, BLOW MY BODY APART FROM THE INSIDE OUT.
TRY IT AGAIN AND IT WILL BE THE LAST TRICK YOU PULL.
YOU CAN'T BE THE ORIGINAL MYSTERIO. QUENTIN BECK IS DEAD. QUENTIN BECK COMMITTED SUICIDE.
QUENTIN BECK DOESN'T DISAGREE.
WHO ARE YOU, THEN? BECK'S OLD FRIEND, DANIEL BERKHART?
NO.
BUT DANIEL'S HERE. HE SHOWED UP A FEW MINUTES AGO. YOUR SMOKE TRICK WAS A BEACON TO HIM.
YOU'VE BEEN HANDED A RARE OPPORTUNITY, FRANCIS, TO PROVE YOURSELF. TO CONQUER NOT ONLY A FELLOW PRETENDER, BUT SPIDER-MAN AS WELL.
MY NEW ASSOCIATES ARE VERY INTERESTED IN THE OUTCOME.

OKAY... ARROW. YOU WAIT HERE WITH THE KIDS.
WHERE DO YOU THINK *YOU'RE* GOING?

I'M TAKING POINT. IF THIS HALLWAY IS BOOBY-TRAPPED, I'M GOING TO TAKE IT FIRST.
BUT WHAT IF SOMETHING HAPPENS TO YOU?

I'LL BE FINE. I'M ABOUT TO SHOW YOU WHY THEY CALL ME "FLASH."
IF IT INVOLVES A LONG RAINCOAT, I'M NOT SURE THIS IS THE *APPROPRIATE* TIME.
CUTE.

24-37-18... AAAAAND...

HIKE!!

HE'S ON THE TWENTY-- THE TEN--
HE'S GOING ALL THE WAY!!!
AND THE CROWD GOES WILD!!!
HUH?
YES, I'D SAY "HUH" PRETTY MUCH COVERS IT.

OKAY, LET'S TRY THAT AGAIN.
WE MIGHT AS WELL ALL GO THIS TIME, SINCE THERE WASN'T ANY KIND OF--
COACH
WHOA!!
NUTS!!!!

HEELLLLPPPP!!
I'M HERE! I'M--
WHY SUCH CONSTERNATION, SPIDER-MAN? IF SHE'S GOOD ENOUGH TO BE *YOUR* BRIDE...
...THEN CERTAINLY SHE IS WORTHY OF BEING *MINE*, EH?
PETER, PLEASE! HELP ME! DON'T LET HIM--!
PETEEEER!
PETER, DO SOMETHING! I--

SPIDER-MAN! WHAT'S HAPPENING?!
NOTHING. NOTHING AT ALL.
YOU WANT HER, DRACULA? FINE. DRAIN HER DRY. BE MY GUEST.
PITY. FOR ONE WHO HAS GAINED SUCH NOTORIETY FOR HUMOR, IT'S DISTRESSING TO SEE WHAT YOU BELIEVE PASSES FOR A JEST.
PETER, YOU...YOU CAN'T BE SERIOUS! YOU'RE BLUFFING! THIS IS A--
NO, IT'S ALL GOOD, HONEY. YOU'LL BE ABLE TO USE YOUR TIME MORE CONSTRUCTIVELY.
ONCE YOU'RE A VAMPIRE, YOU WON'T BE WASTING ENDLESS HOURS STARING INTO THE MIRROR.
PEETERRRRRR!!!
WHA-WHAT ARE YOU DOING?!? HOW COULD YOU...?
IT'S A HOLO-IMAGE. OR A ROBOT. SOMETHING LIKE THAT.
BUT...
WHOEVER BUILT HER FORGOT TO PUT A WEDDING RING ON HER FINGER.
WHAT IF SHE'D BEEN WEARING IT AND IT FELL OFF?

PETER! OH, THANK GOD!
IT'S ALL OVER THE NEWS, THIS CRAZINESS AT THE SCHOOL. WHAT'S HAPPENING THERE?
IT'S MYSTERIO.
I THOUGHT HE WAS DEAD!
AND YOU THOUGHT I WAS DEAD.
YOU WERE. YOU CAME BACK.
THERE Y'GO. IS AUNT MAY WITH YOU?
SHE'S HERE IN THE TOWER, YES. WHY?
JUST CHECKING. I SHOULD'VE THOUGHT TO CALL IMMEDIATELY, BUT I WAS...IN THE MOMENT.
I'M NOT SURE WHAT YOU'RE TALKING ABOUT. ARE YOU GONNA BE OKAY?
SURE. NOTHING I CAN'T HANDLE.
OH...WHAT'S FOR DINNER TONIGHT?
AUNT MAY'S MAKING HER MAC AND CHEESE.
GREAT! I MAY RUN LAT SO SAVE ME SOME.
KLONG

ARROW! GET THE KIDS CLEAR! HURRY!
BUT... WHAT ABOUT Y--?
GO, WILL YA PLEASE?! RUN!
GO! GO!!!
JEREMY!!!
WHAT'RE YOU, STUPID?!? WHAT PART OF "GO" DIDN'T YOU GET?!?

SNIK
SKREEEEE!!!
COACH
SKREEEEEEEEE!!!
C'MON! HURRY!
COACH

WHAT'D YOU STAB HIM WITH?!
MY SWISS ARMY KNIFE. MY DAD GAVE IT TO ME.

YOU'RE NOT SUPPOSED TO HAVE STUFF LIKE THAT IN THE SCHOOL.
ARE...YOU GONNA REPORT ME? THAT I HAD THE KNIFE?

KNIFE? WHAT KNIFE? I DIDN'T SEE ANY KNIFE.
DID YOU SEE A SWISS ARMY KNIFE, MISS ARROW?
COACH

NOPE. ALTHOUGH, YOU HAVE TO WONDER, FOR A COUNTRY THAT'S NEUTRAL, THEY'RE BIG ON ARMY KNIVES. WHAT'S UP WITH--

--THAAAAAAAAT...
HURRY! GET HER OUT!!!
WHAT DOES IT LOOK LIKE I'M DOIN'?!
"HOW LONG YOU GOING TO HIDE, MYSTERIO? HUH?"

C'MON! ENOUGH OF THIS! WHATEVER SICK JOLLIES THIS IS GIVING YOU, YOU KNOW NONE OF THE OTHERS MATTER!
WAIT A MINUTE! I MATTER! WHAT HAPPENS TO ME MATTERS!
YOU KNOW NONE OF THE OTHERS MATTER IN THE STRICT CONTEXT OF OUR INTERPERSONAL DYNAMICS AND YOUR PERSONAL ENMITY FOR ME!
OH. OKAY.
NO MORE SNEAKING AROUND OR MISDIRECTION. YOU AND ME, MANO A MANO! MAN-TO-MAN!
MANO A MANO MEANS "HAND-TO-HAND," YOU IDIOT.
RIGHT. I KNEW THAT. JUST LIKE I KNEW TAUNTING YOU WOULD DRAW YOU OUT.
AND DID YOU KNOW I WOULD QUICKLY AND EASILY KILL YOU?
I KNEW YOU'D TRY.
AND DID YOU KNOW THAT I, THE TRUE MYSTERIO, WOULD SHOW UP TO AID YOU IN THRASHING THIS CHARLATAN TO WITHIN AN INCH OF HIS LIFE...
...AND THEN DRAG HIM TWO MORE INCHES?

OOOOF!
HELLO. YOU SEEM TO BE AN INNOCENT BYSTANDER IN ALL THIS.
THEN AGAIN, "SEEM" IS SUCH A SUBTLE WORD. AS IN, THINGS ARE NOT ALWAYS WHAT THEY SEEM.
ISN'T THAT THE CASE, MISS ARROW?
WHO ARE YOU?
QUENTIN BECK. ALSO KNOWN AS "MYSTERIO."
PERHAPS YOU HEARD THAT I WAS DEAD. THAT I'D TAKEN A GUN AND BLOWN MY BRAINS OUT.
LET ME GUESS. THE REPORTS OF YOUR DEATH ARE GREATLY EXAGGERATED.
AS A MATTER OF FACT...

...NOT *THAT* GREATLY, NO.

FRIENDLY NEIGHBORHOOD SPIDER-MAN #13

HERE, GUYS! THE FRONT DOORS! WE MADE IT!
NOW I WANT YOU GUYS TO GO THROUGH AND RUN OUT OF HERE AS FAST AS YOU CAN!
WHAT ABOUT YOU, COACH? WHAT ABOUT MISS ARROW?
PRINCE of SPACE
I AIN'T OUTTA HERE UNTIL I FIND HER. HER AND SPIDEY.
RIGHT. MR. PAR--
YOU MEAN MR. PARKER?
JEEZ. HE... HE REALLY IS SPIDEY, ISN'T HE?
WELL... SURE, COACH! WHERE'VE YOU BEEN?
IT'S JUST THAT--
NEVER MIND. JUST GO. NOW.
BUT--
NO "BUTS!" YOU GET YOUR BUTTS IN GEAR OR TOMORROW THE BUNCH OF YOU ARE GONNA BE GIVING ME A HUNDRED PUSH-UPS EACH!
YESSIR!

UNHHH...
NOW THAT THE KIDS ARE SAFE, I GOTTA FIND A WAY TO HELP ARROW...

"...NOT TO MENTION OUR FRIENDLY NEIGHBORHOOD SPIDER-MAN."
DO YOU HAVE ANY IDEA HOW RIDICULOUS YOU LOOK IN THAT OUTFIT?
YOU'RE THE ONE WHO IS CLEARLY ABSURDLY ATTIRED!
OKAY, THIS IS JUST SO DRENCHED IN IRONY, I DON'T EVEN KNOW WHERE TO BEGIN.

ROGER...I NEED YOU TO DO SOMETHING FOR ME.
ME?
YEAH.
A.V. ROOM
STAY HERE UNTIL I SAY IT'S SAFE TO COME OUT.
A.V. ROOM
ALL... ALL RIGHT. I THINK I CAN DO THAT.
YOU'RE NOTHING BUT A RAT, KLUM. A LITTLE RAT, SCURRYING AROUND AND NIBBLING ON THE ACCOUTREMENTS OF YOUR BETTERS.
NOT FOR LONG...
KLUM? ARE YOU SAYING THAT'S...FRANCIS KLUM...?
BECAUSE I HAVE *JUST* THE THING TO DEAL WITH RATS!

OH NO! GIANT SNAKES! WHATEVER WILL I DO?
AM I PANICKING YET? AM I TREMBLING IN YOUR PRESENCE?
WHAT'S THAT? I'M NOT? FANCY THAT!
ARHHHH!!

ANYTHING... YOU...CAN THROW AT ME...
...I...CAN COUNTER!
UNHHHH!!!
A...A NICE TRICK... BUT IT WON'T SAVE YOU...
YOU'RE THE ONE... WHO'LL NEED SAVING...
BOY, THE YANKEES SURE GOT SHELLACKED LAST NIGHT.

IT'S...IT'S TRICK! SOME KIND OF--
I...I MEAN, THAT'S WHAT YOU'RE ALL ABOUT, RIGHT? TRICKS AND ILLUSIONS...
YOU'RE... YOU'RE TRYING TO TELL ME YOU'RE... DEAD?
NO TRICK. NO ILLUSION.

I PREFER TO THINK OF IT AS AN "AGING ALTERNATIVE."
BUT THE UNIVERSE DESPISES WASTE, MISS ARROW. SIMPLY BECAUSE I WAS DONE WITH LIFE...
...AS IT TURNS OUT, LIFE WASN'T DONE WITH ME.

OR "AFTER-LIFE," MORE PROPERLY. AFTER ALL, WE ALL KNOW WHERE SUICIDES WIND UP. AND AS IT TURNS OUT...
...THERE WERE CERTAIN INDIVIDUALS WHO FELT THAT I COULD SERVE THEIR NEEDS. WE ALL DO OUR PARTS IN THE COSMIC SCHEME OF THINGS, DON'T WE?
BUT THEN, I DON'T HAVE TO TELL YOU THAT.

I...I DON'T KNOW WHAT YOU'RE TALKING ABOUT. YOU'RE CRAZY!

IS THAT YOUR STORY? ARE YOU STICKING TO IT?
YOU LIKE TO PLAY GAMES, THEN. VERY WELL...
I'VE ALWAYS LIKED GAMES.

LET'S PLAY "ASHES, ASHES, WE ALL FALL DOWN."

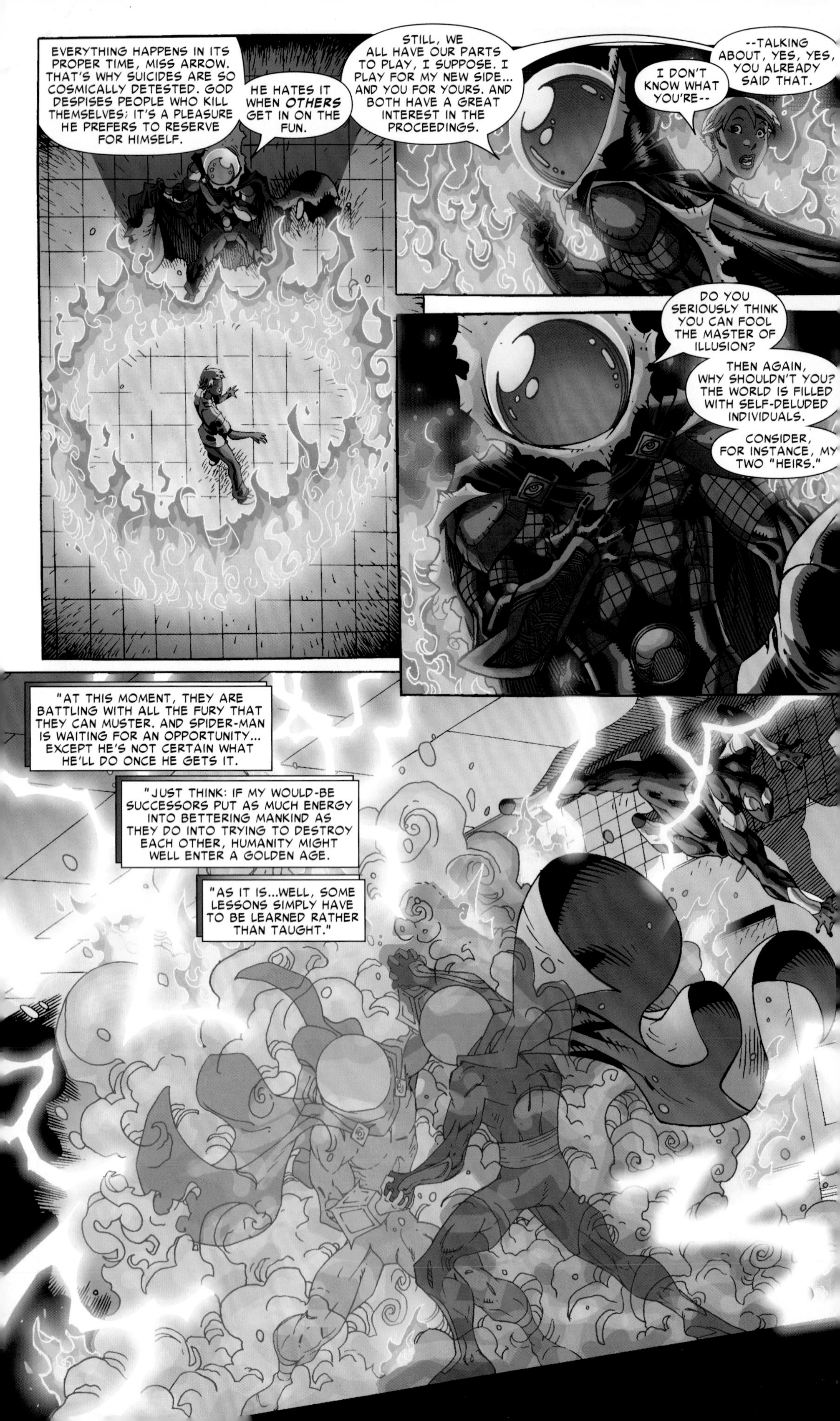
EVERYTHING HAPPENS IN ITS PROPER TIME, MISS ARROW. THAT'S WHY SUICIDES ARE SO COSMICALLY DETESTED. GOD DESPISES PEOPLE WHO KILL THEMSELVES; IT'S A PLEASURE HE PREFERS TO RESERVE FOR HIMSELF.
HE HATES IT WHEN *OTHERS* GET IN ON THE FUN.
STILL, WE ALL HAVE OUR PARTS TO PLAY, I SUPPOSE. I PLAY FOR MY NEW SIDE... AND YOU FOR YOURS. AND BOTH HAVE A GREAT INTEREST IN THE PROCEEDINGS.
I DON'T KNOW WHAT YOU'RE--
--TALKING ABOUT, YES, YES, YOU ALREADY SAID THAT.
DO YOU SERIOUSLY THINK YOU CAN FOOL THE MASTER OF ILLUSION?
THEN AGAIN, WHY SHOULDN'T YOU? THE WORLD IS FILLED WITH SELF-DELUDED INDIVIDUALS.
CONSIDER, FOR INSTANCE, MY TWO "HEIRS."
"AT THIS MOMENT, THEY ARE BATTLING WITH ALL THE FURY THAT THEY CAN MUSTER. AND SPIDER-MAN IS WAITING FOR AN OPPORTUNITY... EXCEPT HE'S NOT CERTAIN WHAT HE'LL DO ONCE HE GETS IT.
"JUST THINK: IF MY WOULD-BE SUCCESSORS PUT AS MUCH ENERGY INTO BETTERING MANKIND AS THEY DO INTO TRYING TO DESTROY EACH OTHER, HUMANITY MIGHT WELL ENTER A GOLDEN AGE.
"AS IT IS...WELL, SOME LESSONS SIMPLY HAVE TO BE LEARNED RATHER THAN TAUGHT."

HUNH HUNH
YOU GAVE IT A GOOD EFFORT, KLUM. YOU HAVE A GREAT DEAL OF NATURAL SKILL.
IF I THOUGHT I COULD TRUST YOU, YOU MIGHT EVEN HAVE MADE A WORTHY APPRENTICE.
WHAT--?
THWIPP
MULTIPLE MYSTERIOS IS BAD ENOUGH. NOW WE'RE GONNA HAVE A BUNCH OF DONALD TRUMPS? I DON'T THINK SO.
AND I DON'T THINK YOU REMEMBER THAT I CAN DISSOLVE YOUR WEBBING AT WILL.
YOU'RE MAKING A FOOLISH MISTAKE, PARKER. HELP ME FINISH OFF THIS FOOL...EARN AT LEAST A TEMPORARY DETENTE...
OTHERWISE, WITH YOUR IDENTITY KNOWN, TIME IS ON MY SIDE. SOONER OR LATER, I'LL--
FORGET IT, MISTY. I'VE ALWAYS BEEN MORE OF A SOONER-THAN-LATER KINDA GUY.
SO HOW ABOUT I CLEAN YOUR CLOCK SOONER AND LET LATER SORT ITSELF OUT?

OOOO! ONE OF YOUR PATENTED "NOW YOU SEE ME, NOW YOU DON'T" CLOUDS! THE KIND THAT SCREWS UP EVEN MY SPIDER-SENSE!
HERE'S THE FUNNY THING: FIRST, MY SPIDER-SENSE IS MORE HEIGHTENED THAN EVER. SECOND, I'VE GOT SOME ON-BOARD TRACKING TECHNOLOGY THAT CAN'T BE BEAT.
BETWEEN THE TWO OF THOSE...
WAAAM
...THINGS HAVE CHANGED.
UNNFFFF!

SEE, I FIGURE IF YOU'RE TOUGH ENOUGH TO TAKE OUT YOUR RIVAL...THEN YOU'RE THE ONE I SHOULD BE WORRYING ABOUT.
YOU THOUGHT CORRECTLY.
MY LITTLE FRIENDS ARE POISONED, SPIDER-MAN! THE SLIGHTEST SCRATCH--
--WOULD BE REALLY NASTY IF I LET THEM GET ANY-WHERE NEAR...WHICH I'M NOT ABOUT TO DO.
SEE, I'VE UNDERGONE SOME CHANGES SINCE WE LAST DANCED. I'M FASTER...
...AND STRONGER!
KRAAAK

ILLUSIONS ARE GREAT AND ALL, BUT YOU CAN'T BEAT REAL LIFE.
AND YOU CAN'T BEAT ME.
NOR COULD THAT FOOL. BUT I REALIZED THERE WAS NO POINT EXPENDING ENERGY AGAINST HIM.
I SIMPLY ALLOWED HIM TO THINK HE HAD ME ON THE ROPES...KNOWING THAT YOU'D STEP IN TO DEFEAT HIM FOR ME.
YOUR PATHETIC INTEREST IN HELPING THOSE "IN NEED" IS JUST THAT PREDICTABLE...EVEN WHEN SOMEONE DOESN'T NEED YOUR HELP.
I JUST NEED YOU DEAD.
IT'S WHAT YOU DESERVE...FOR WHAT YOU DID TO MY BROTHER.
YOU THINK I'M JUST GONNA STAND HERE AND LET YOU STAB ME?
NOT AT ALL. I THINK YOU'RE GOING TO PICK IT UP...
AND KILL YOURSELF WITH IT.
RIGHT NOW.

N-NO...
YES.
UNLESS YOU'RE UNDER THE IMPRESSION THAT WHATEVER "IMPROVEMENTS" THERE MAY BE IN YOUR POWER... IS SUFFICIENT TO WITH-STAND MINE.
EVERY MYSTERIO UNTIL NOW HAS RELIED ON TRICKS. IN MY CASE, THEY MERELY AUGMENT MY POWER.
I COULD TELEPORT MY FIST INTO YOUR HEAD. BUT THAT WOULD BE TOO SIMPLE, TOO--
WHA--?
ARRHHH!!

Y'LIKE THAT? THAT'S NOTHIN'! YOU'RE LUCKY I AIN'T HOLDING A DODGEBALL!
FOOL! YOU'VE JUST KILLED EVERY-ONE IN THIS SCHOOL.
WHAT...?
I WASN'T LYING WHEN I SAID THERE WAS A BOMB IN THE SCHOOL. IT'S IN THE BASEMENT, NEAR THE FURNACE.
AND I'VE JUST REMOTE-ACTIVATED IT.
COACH
WHEN IT GOES OFF IN JUST UNDER THREE MINUTES, THE ENTIRE BLOCK WILL GO UP.
I, OF COURSE, WILL HAVE TELEPORTED TO SAFETY. EVERYONE ELSE WON'T BE AS FORTUNATE.
OF COURSE, I COULD BE BLUFFING. CARE TO CALL ME ON IT?
I *THOUGHT* NOT.
DAMNATION. CAN'T FOCUS MY POWER...THROUGH THE PAIN...
THE SIMPLER APPROACH IS STARTING TO LOOK...A LOT BETTER...
ARRRHHH!

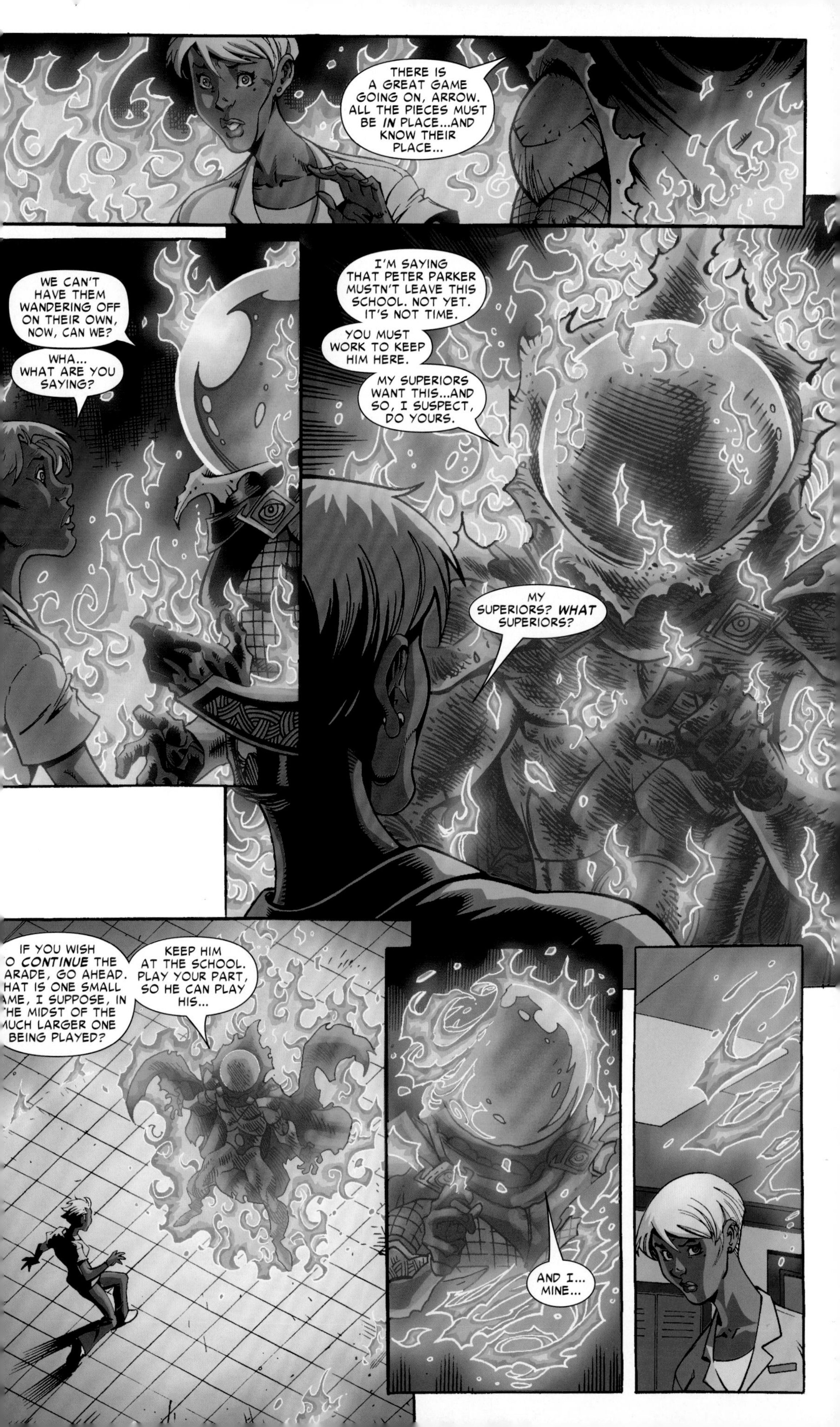
THERE IS A GREAT GAME GOING ON, ARROW. ALL THE PIECES MUST BE *IN* PLACE...AND KNOW THEIR PLACE...
WE CAN'T HAVE THEM WANDERING OFF ON THEIR OWN, NOW, CAN WE?
WHA... WHAT ARE YOU SAYING?
I'M SAYING THAT PETER PARKER MUSTN'T LEAVE THIS SCHOOL. NOT YET. IT'S NOT TIME.
YOU MUST WORK TO KEEP HIM HERE.
MY SUPERIORS WANT THIS...AND SO, I SUSPECT, DO YOURS.
MY SUPERIORS? **WHAT** SUPERIORS?
IF YOU WISH O *CONTINUE* THE ARADE, GO AHEAD. HAT IS ONE SMALL AME, I SUPPOSE, IN HE MIDST OF THE MUCH LARGER ONE BEING PLAYED?
KEEP HIM AT THE SCHOOL. PLAY YOUR PART, SO HE CAN PLAY HIS...
AND I... MINE...

PETE--!
CAN I... Y'KNOW...CALL YOU PETE? OR SHOULD IT BE SPIDEY? OR...
FLASH, YOU SAVED MY BUTT BACK THERE. MYSTERIO HAD ME ON THE ROPES. YOU CAN CALL ME HARVEY THE WONDER HAMSTER IF YOU WANT.
WATCH YOUR BACK, THOUGH. MYSTERIO WAS SO FOCUSED ON ME THAT YOU CAUGHT HIM OFF GUARD. YOU WON'T GET THAT LUCKY AGAIN.
I'M NOT AFRAID OF OL' BUBBLEHEAD.
THAT'S YOUR FIRST MISTAKE. DON'T MAKE IT YOUR LAST.
AFTER I GET THIS SQUARED AWAY, WE GOTTA FIND THE KIDS.
THEY'RE SAFE. I GOT 'EM OUT OF THE SCHOOL.
REALLY? WOW. BETWEEN THAT AND BAILING ME OUT, YOU'R HAVING A GREAT DAY. HEY, UH...SORRY ABOU REARRANGING YOUR FACE EARLIER...
DON'T SWEAT IT. I PROBABLY HAD IT COMING.
NO "PROBABLY" ABOUT IT. STILL... I'M SORRY.

OKAY...DON'T HAVE A LOT OF TIME HERE...BUT THE MECHANISM DOESN'T LOOK TOO COMPLICATED.
WELL, THEN WE'LL HAVE TO MAKE IT A BIT MORE CHALLENGING, WON'T WE?
WHA...?
IT'LL TAKE YOU ONLY A FEW SECONDS TO JUMP UP AND CUT HIM DOWN... BUT YOU'LL NEED THAT TIME TO DEFUSE THE BOMB. MEANTIME, I'LL HAVE MY REVENGE ON YOUR KNIFE-THROWING FRIEND.
F-forget m-uh...uh...
THWIP
AH, SO YOU LEAVE HIM TO DIE. A WISE, IF TRAGIC, CHOICE.

I'LL SAY THIS FOR ALL YOU FREAKIN' MYSTERIOS...
YOU JUST DON'T KNOW WHEN TO SHUT UP.
BY THE WAY, YOU MIGHT BE WANTING THIS.
TOOK ME ABOUT THREE SECONDS TO STOP IT.
00:04
AND THAT'S ABOUT HOW LONG IT'LL TAKE ME TO PUT PAID TO YOU, ONCE I GET MY HANDS ON YOU.
YOU MIGHT WANT TO CONSIDER SURRENDERING NOW, FRANCIS.
NOW THAT I KNOW IT'S YOU, I'VE SET CYBERNETIC SCRAMBLING CIRCUITRY IN MY COSTUME THAT'LL BLOCK YOUR MENTAL COMMANDS.
AND YOUR ATTEMPTS TO AMBUSH ME VIA TELEPORTATION WON'T WORK, BECAUSE MY HEIGHTENED SPIDER-SENSE AND ON-BOARD TRACKING SENSORS WILL WARN ME.
IF YOU'RE SMART, YOU'LL GIVE UP NOW.
You... can do all that?
NO. I'M JUST USING MY MOST *DANGEROUS* POWER OF ALL: MY SPIDER-BULL.

"GIVE UP NOW." SMUG, ARROGANT FOOL.
THIS GAME IS BARELY BEGUN.
HE THINKS HIS SPIDER-SENSE WILL SAVE HIM?
NOTHING WILL SAVE HIM. NOT IN--
LIBRARY
WELL, WELL. WHAT HAVE WE HERE?
YOU...YOU KEEP AWAY FROM ME.
WOULD THAT I COULD, MY DEAR.
BUT YOU'RE ABOUT TO BECOME A PAWN IN A MUCH LARGER GAME.
NO! LET GO!
YOU CAN FIGHT IF YOU WISH. IN FACT, I'D PREFER IT IF YOU DID...

KCHHH
KOFF
KOFFFFF
WHA... WHAT...DID YOU...
I AM SICK OF MYSTERIOS LECTURING ME ABOUT GAMES.
DAMN SICK.
WHAT... ARE YOU...?
I'LL TELL YOU WHAT I'M NOT.
I'M NOBODY'S PAWN.

AAAAAAAAAA....!!
Arrow!
FLASH! OH....THANK GOD!
HE WAS HERE! THAT...THAT MYSTERIO CREATURE! I THOUGHT HE WAS GOING TO KILL ME!
We heard you scream.
ACTUALLY, I THOUGHT I HEARD A GUY SCREAM.
NO, IT WAS ME. BUT THEN HE JUST...HE COLLAPSED, CLUTCHING WHAT LOOKED LIKE A WOUND IN HIS SHOULDER. AND THEN HE JUST...JUST VANISHED.
WHAT...WHAT HAPPENED TO YOUR VOICE?
Ohh...a little strangulation. Nothing serious.
AND THE CHILDREN! THEY'RE ALL RIGHT?
I got 'em out of the building.
WELL, THEN...

"...LET'S MAKE SURE THEY'RE OKAY."
108
ARE THEY...?
THEY'RE JUST UNCONSCIOUS. MY ON-BOARD OXYGEN SYSTEM IS PROTECTING ME FROM THE MIST...AND IT'S STARTING TO DISSIPATE ANYWAY.
JUST LIKE THE REST OF THIS "HAUNTED HOUSE" SCENARIO SHUT DOWN WHEN MYSTERIO BOOKED IT OUTTA HERE. HE MUST'VE HAD REMOTE CONTROLS IN HIS COSTUME.
YOU KNOW SO MUCH ABOUT THESE THINGS.
YEAH, WELL... WHEN Y'HANG AROUND SPIDEY, YOU JUST PICK STUFF UP. HECK, HE AND I GO BACK A LONG--
YOU WERE VERY BRAVE. AND YOU KNOW WHAT ELSE?
WHAT?
I'M GOING TO FIND A WAY TO CONVINCE PETER TO STAY. WE NEED HIM.
"SOUNDS LIKE A PLAN."
A.V. ROOM
UHM... HELLO?
IS IT SAFE YET?
JUST LET ME KNOW WHEN IT IS, OKAY?
RIGHT. I'LL JUS WAIT HER THEN.

THE STORY SO FAR...

Once again, life has changed considerably for Peter Parker. Following a run-in with the demon Mephisto, Peter Parker's identity is under wraps once more. However, he is no longer wedded to Mary Jane as the arch-demon took all memory of their marriage. Neither is he an active member of the Avengers.

Aunt May has found love in the form of Jay Jameson, the father of former-Daily-Bugle-editor-now-Mayor Jonah Jameson. The pair have just wed and are currently on their honeymoon.

A new name in organised crime has appeared in New York City as well, in the form of the mysterious Mr. Negative. With the Maggia weakened, he has recently made a move against them to shift the balance of power in his favour. However, few know that Mr. Negative is the alias of Martin Li, a philanthropic gentleman who runs a soup kitchen in Chinatown – the FEAST Project – where Peter's Aunt May volunteers.

MARVEL
618 .com

the AMAZING SPIDER-MAN

#618

HE PAST FEW YEARS HAVE NOT BEEN KIND TO THE MAGGIA CRIME FAMILY.
IT STARTED AT THE OLD EMPYREAN OPERA HOUSE...
...WHEN UNDERBOSS ALBERTO KARNELLI WAS GUNNED DOWN IN THE MIDDLE OF HIS FAVORITE ARIA.

NEXT THERE WAS CONSIGLIERE EDDIE COSTA.
HE WENT FACE FIRST INTO A PLATE OF POISONED CAPELLINI.

SOON AFTER THAT, CAPO MILO MANFREDI HAD A LITTLE "CAR TROUBLE" ON HIS WAY TO A COURT HEARING.

LATER, ENFORCER TONY "TWO-STEP" GALLO FOUND A QUICK WAY TO SHORTEN HIS LIFE SENTENCE.

NUMBERS MAN PAULO MUNOZ WENT MISSING FOR A WHILE, TILL HE SHOWED UP AT THE ZOO'S REPTILE HOUSE...
DON'T FEED THE ANIMALS
...AS A LEFT EAR, A LOAFER, AND TWO HUNDRED POUNDS OF ALLIGATOR DROPPINGS.

THEN JOE KARNELLI JUNIOR LEFT THE BUSINESS THE SAME WAY HE CAME INTO IT: IN CONSTRUCTION.

VINCENZO KARNELLI WAS ON HAND WHEN HIS GENTLEMAN'S CLUB BURNED DOWN.
THEY HAD TO HAVE A CLOSED COFFIN CEREMONY.

AS DID FOUR MADE MEN FROM THE MANFREDI CLAN.
NOBODY LIKES TO TALK ABOUT WHAT THEY WERE MADE INTO.
OR WHY THE OFFICERS WHO FOUND 'EM STOPPED BUYING CHOPS FROM FERRARA'S BUTCHER SHOP.

AND THEN THERE WAS THAT INCIDENT AT THE SCRAP YARD A FEW MONTHS AGO WITH SILVIO MANFREDI...
AHHH!
HE WAS DON OF THE ENTIRE FAMILY. MOST PEOPLE CALLED HIM BY HIS OTHER NAME, SILVERMANE. YOU KNOW
...THAT OLD GUY IN THE BIG, METAL ROBOT SUIT.
HAMMERHEAD! GET ME DOWN FROM HERE!
IN A SEC, BOSS! LOOKS LIKE THE OWL'S GOONS ARE MAKIN' THEIR MOVE!

HAMMERHEAD!
DON MANFREDI!?
JOSEPH! DO SOMETHING!!
SILVER-MANE!
BOSS! NO!!
KRRRRRRKRRKKRRKKRKYEEEKKRRNCHKLANGKRRRCCHHHKK
KRUNCH

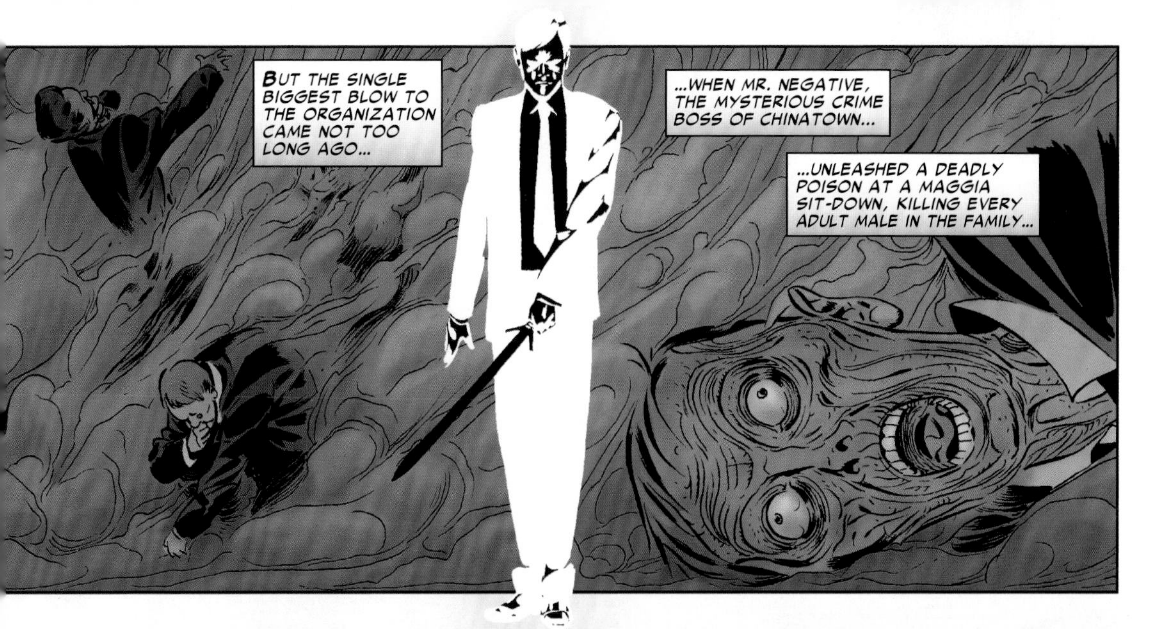
BUT THE SINGLE BIGGEST BLOW TO THE ORGANIZATION CAME NOT TOO LONG AGO...
...WHEN MR. NEGATIVE, THE MYSTERIOUS CRIME BOSS OF CHINATOWN...
...UNLEASHED A DEADLY POISON AT A MAGGIA SIT-DOWN, KILLING EVERY ADULT MALE IN THE FAMILY...

AVE THIS GUY: BABY UNO KARNELLI, A MAN O'S TURNED "ORGANIZED ME" INTO AN OXYMORON.
SO WITH NEGATIVE'S UYS MAKING MORE D MORE HITS ON OUR ITIMATE BUSINESSES, E'RE RUNNING OUTTA VAYS TO LAUNDER OUR MONEY.
BUT DON'T WORRY, I GOT A PLAN! IT'S LIKE THIS...
$100

WE USE THAT CASH IN OUR UNDERGROUND CASINOS. GAMBLERS WILL GIVE US CLEAN BILLS FOR CHIPS...
AND THEN WE'LL PAY 'EM OUT IN DIRTY MONEY. SMART, HUH? EVEN WHEN WE LOSE, IT'S A WIN-WIN.
THAT OLD GAG? DON KARNELLI, NOBODY DOES THAT ANYMORE.
BRUNO, YOU CAN'T--
CARMINE, YOU'RE HIS CONSIGLIERE, TALK SOME SENSE INTO 'IM.
LISTEN TO ME, BRUNO, IT WON'T WORK.

TAKE THAT BANK JOB WE DID LAST MONTH. A LOT OF THAT'S IN SEQUENTIAL BILLS.
WE START MOVING THAT THROUGH OUR GAMBLING DENS, THE COPS WILL TRACE IT BACK TO US.
OR WORSE, MR. NEGATIVE WILL.

GEEZ, CARMINE. YOU WORRY TOO MUCH. TAKE A CHANCE. LIVE A LITTLE.

LOOKIT ALLA' THESE FRICKIN' KUNG FU GUYS! THEY'RE *EVERYWHERE!*
THEY'RE MR. NEGATIVE'S INNER-DEMONS.
WHATEVER! THEY'RE SLAUGHTERIN' US! *DAMN IT,* CARMINE. YOU GOT THE BRAINS, YOU SHOULD BE CALLIN' THE SHOTS! NOT THAT CRAZY-@#% BRUNO!
HE'S GOT THE KARNELL BLOOD, SAL. IN THE MAGGIA, THAT BEATS BRAINS.
GAHH!

THE HELL?! HAMMERHEAD?! WHAT'RE YOU DOIN' WITH THESE PUNKS?! YOU'RE A MAGGIA GUY! YOU'RE-- MMPH!
NOT ANYMORE. I TRADED UP!

HM. GUESS I CAN'T BLAME YA. ALL THINGS CONSIDERED...

...SEEMS LIKE A PRETTY SMART MOVE.
ZZAWW
THWIP

HEY, LOOK HERE! IT'S SPIDER-MAN! AND HE'S ON OUR SIDE!
OH-HO-NO! DON'T EVEN!
I'D DO THIS FOR ANYONE! A-N-Y-O-N-E! CAPEESH?!!
MYSTERIOSO Part 1
UN-MURDER INCORPORATED
WRITER Dan SLOTT
ARTIST Marcos MARTIN
COLORS Javier RODRIGUEZ
LETTERS Joe CARAMAGNA
TOM BRENNAN ASST EDITOR
STEPHEN WACKER GAMBLER
ALAN FINE EXECUTIVE PRODUCER
TOM BREVOORT EXECUTIVE EDITOR
JOE QUESADA EDITOR-IN-CHIEF
DAN BUCKLEY PUBLISHER
GALE, KELLY, SLOTT, VAN LENTE, WAID & WELLS WEBHEADS
HILTON
NINE
BIG 6
BIG 8
PAYS DOUBLE
10
Seven

I'M AN EQUAL OPPORTUNITY LIFE-SAVING KINDA GUY.
DAMSELS IN DISTRESS, DOGS THAT RUN INTO TRAFFIC, EVEN DIRTBAGS LIKE YOU.
SAL, YOU OKAY?
YEAH. HOW'D THE WALL-CRAWLER GET HERE?
MUST A' BEEN TRACKIN' NEGATIVE'S GUYS. HE COULD CARE LESS ABOUT THE MAGGIA.
WE'RE JUST A BIG JOKE TO HIM. THAT'S ALL WE ARE ANYMORE. ONE BIG JOKE.
HAMMERHEAD! LONG TIME, NO SEE, FLATTOP! I'L GET TO YOU IN A SE HERE, TAKE A NUMBER. TAKE 38 OF 'EM.

OOMPH--
HEY, HERE'S A FUN GAME. LET'S PLAY 52 PICKUP! WITH YOUR TEETH.
THWAK
PLAYER

ALL RIGHT YOU GUYS. WE'RE DONE HERE.
BUT MR. NEGATIVE SAID--

NEGATIVE PUT ME IN CHARGE. I'M HIS HAMMER.
HE WANTED THIS PLACE BROKEN. WELL IT'S BROKE.

C'MON!
AW. WAS IT SOMETHING I SAID?

LOOKS LIKE YOUR PLAYMATES ARE TAKING OFF. AND THE MAGGIA-BOYS, TOO.
COULDN'T MAKE MY LIFE EASIER AND ALL GO IN THE SAME DIRECTION, COULD YOU?

SEE YA AROUND, WALL-CRAWLER! AND THANKS FOR THE ASSIST.
YOU'RE GOOD PEOPLE.
Tony's

WHAT? SPIDEY'S WORKIN' FOR THE MOB NOW?
THE MAYOR'S RIGHT. GUY'S A MENACE.
WAIT, IT'S NOT LIKE THAT. I'M A GOOD GUY!
THAT MEANS I GOTTA SAVE EVERYBODY. EVEN BAD GUYS, RIGHT?

GO STUFF YOURSELF.
OUCH.

TOUGH ROOM.

ONLY BABY BRUNO WOULD THINK OF STUFFIN' HIS CASH IN A MATTRESS SHOWROOM.
PIGGY BANK STORE MUSTA' BEEN CLOSED.
HEY, YOU THINK IT'S SAFE TO LEAVE COOPER ALONE WITH ALL THAT "EVIDENCE"?
HEAR SHE'S BEEN SKIRTIN' THE RULES LATELY.
CAN'T BELIEVE SHE'S RAY COOPER'S KID. NOW HE WAS A GOOD COP.

LIKE I CAN'T HEAR YOU? GEEZ.
SMELLS FISHY.
THAT A CLUE?
YOU NEVER CAN TELL--

PETER? HI! WHAT'RE YOU DOING HERE?
HEY, CARLIE. THOUGHT I MIGHT PICK UP SOME FREELANCE SHOTS FOR FRONT LINE...
POLICE LINE DO NOT

...AND TAKE MY FAVORITE C.S.I. GAL OUT FOR LUNCH. SAY, YOU CHANGED YOUR HAIR.
YOU NOTICED.
YEAH. LOOKS CUTE. SO HOW 'BOUT IT?
UM. OKAY.
WAIT. WHAT AM I DOING?
NOT CROSS

I WANTED TO GET SOME INFO BEFORE NEGATIVE'S GOONS SLAUGHTER MORE MAGGIA GUYS...
...BUT THIS ISN'T RIGHT. CARLIE'S INTO ME AS PETE. BUT AS SPIDEY I'VE BEEN SEEING BLACK CAT.
I REALLY COULD USE A LEAD, BUT...

...BASICALLY THIS'S A MAGGIA STASH HOUSE. WE TRACKED SOME STOLEN CASH HERE. BUT I THINK SOMEONE ON THE FORCE TIPPED OFF MR. NEGATIVE ABOUT IT.
SO, EVEN AFTER WE ROUNDED UP VIN AND ALL OF THOSE DIRTY COPS, THERE'S STILL A LEAK IN THE DEPARTMENT.

AH WELL. GUESS THE HONEYMOON'S OVER.
AUNT MAY!
I TOTALLY FORGOT! I'M SUPPOSED TO PICK HER AND JAY UP AT THE AIRPORT!

RANDY ROBERTSON EVEN LOANED ME HIS CAR. LOOK, I GOTTA GO. WE'LL DO LUNCH SOME OTHER TIME?
SURE.

GOD, WHY AM I SUCH A DOORMAT AROUND HIM?
HE CAN BE SUCH A JERK SOMETIMES. MAYBE I SHOULD JUST FORGET ABOUT PETER PARKER. AFTER ALL...

...THERE'S GOTTA BE SOMEONE OUT THERE WHO'S INTERESTED IN ME.
"HE'S GOING TO BE THE DEATH OF US ISN'T HE?"

I KNOW YOUR NEPHEW MEANS WELL, BUT...
YES, DEAR.
PETER, NOT THAT I'M BACK-SEAT DRIVING, BUT YOU DO KNOW HOW, DON'T YOU?

YEP! SURPRISE! PRETTY GOOD, HUH? A WHILE BACK I ALMOST GOT A TAXI LICENSE.
YEAH. IT DIDN'T WORK OUT.
"ALMOST"?
PETER, WHY DON'T YOU PULL OVER UP HERE?

F.E.A.S.T PROJECT
IT'S BEEN WEEKS SINCE I CHECKED IN WITH EVERYONE AT THE F.E.A.S.T. CENTER.
SCREEEEE
SURE THING, AUNT MAY. HERE'S A LITTLE CURBSIDE SERVICE FOR YA.

THANK THE LORD!
SO, YOU WANT ME TO WAIT? KEEP THE OL' METER RUNNING?

NO, THAT'S FINE, DEAR. YOU CAN GO ON TO JAY'S APARTMENT WITHOUT ME. IT'LL GIVE YOU TWO A CHANCE TO BOND.
MAYYY!
AND BESIDES...

..I'M SURE MY BOSS, ARTIN LI, AND I HAVE A LOT OF CATCHING UP TO DO."

SO YOU'RE SAYING SPIDER-MAN INTERFERED WITH MY PLANS. AGAIN.
AND? HOW DID YOU DISPATCH HIM?

UM... WE DIDN'T, BOSS.

WE CAME STRAIGHT TO YOU. THOUGHT YOU'D WANNA KNOW.
THAT SPIDER-MAN HAS CHALLENGED MY AUTHORITY. AND STILL LIVES.
WELL, YEAH. WHAT'D YOU EXPECT? HE'S SPIDER-MAN.
AND THERE WAS ONLY A HANDFUL OF US.

SHOULDN'T A' SAID THAT.

I WILL ACCEPT NO EXCUSES.

SHZZ

WAIT! I DIDN'T MEAN--

YOU ARE MY INNER-DEMONS. YOU CANNOT DIE.
HE IS A MAN. YOU WISH TO KILL HIM? STRIKE EVERY TIME...
SLSHH

"...RIGHT AT HIS HEART!"
MAY!
WELCOME BACK, MRS. PARKER.
AH! IT'S MRS. JAMESON NOW.
HOW WAS THE HONEYMOON?
JUST WONDERFUL. WE'LL TALK LATER. I JUST WANT TO SAY HELLO TO...

...MARTIN?
MAYBE HE'S IN THE BACK. NOW LET'S SEE, BACK WHEN MARTIN THOUGHT HE MIGHT BE MAYOR...

...HE GAVE ME ALL THE CODES TO RUN THIS PLACE WITHOUT HIM...

WHAT?!

MR. LI? IS THAT YOU?

WAIT! ONE SECOND...

UM...I CAN EXPLAIN...
GNHHH

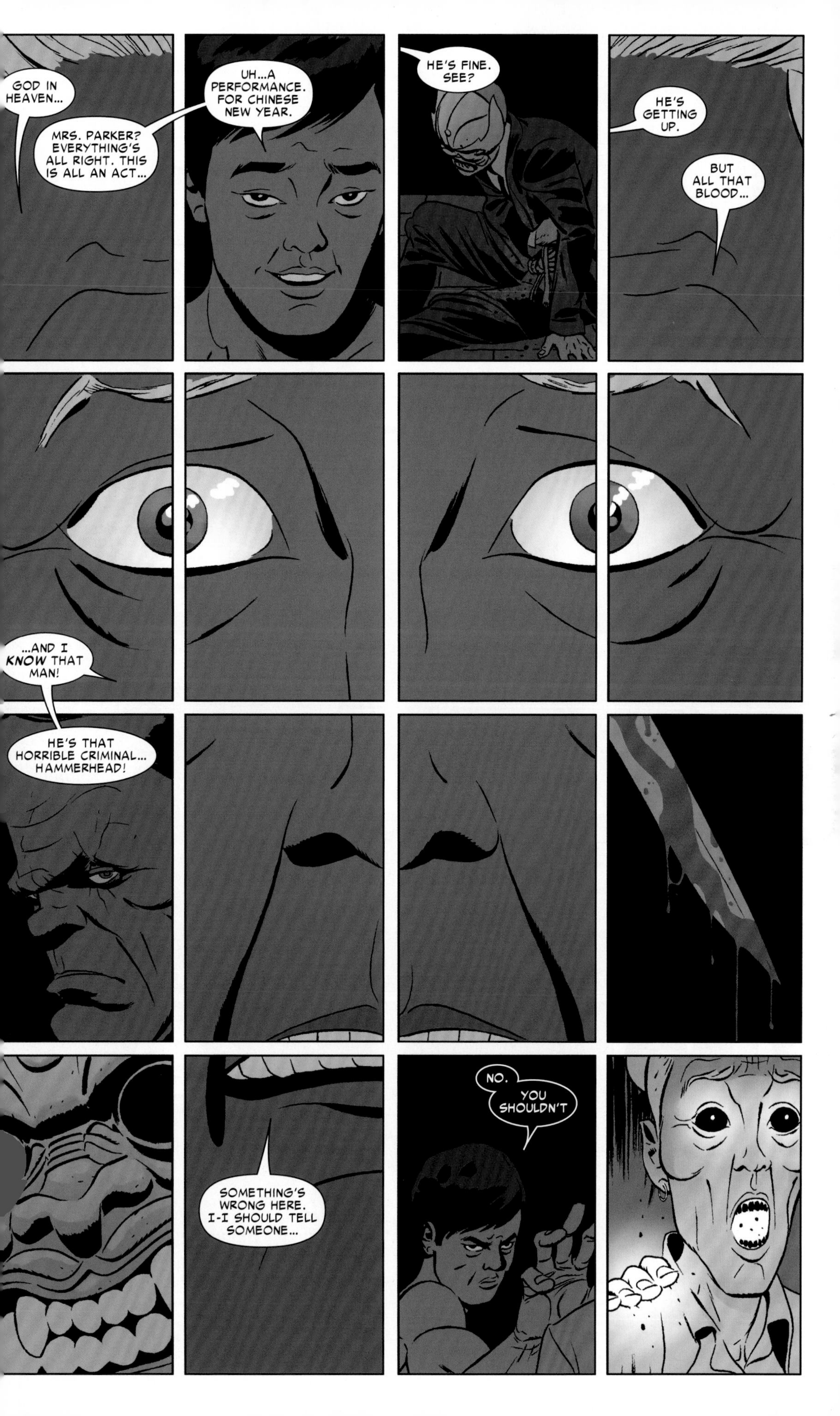
GOD IN HEAVEN...
MRS. PARKER? EVERYTHING'S ALL RIGHT. THIS IS ALL AN ACT...
UH...A PERFORMANCE. FOR CHINESE NEW YEAR.
HE'S FINE. SEE?
HE'S GETTING UP.
BUT ALL THAT BLOOD...
...AND I *KNOW* THAT MAN!
HE'S THAT HORRIBLE CRIMINAL... HAMMERHEAD!
SOMETHING'S WRONG HERE. I-I SHOULD TELL SOMEONE...
NO.
YOU SHOULDN'T

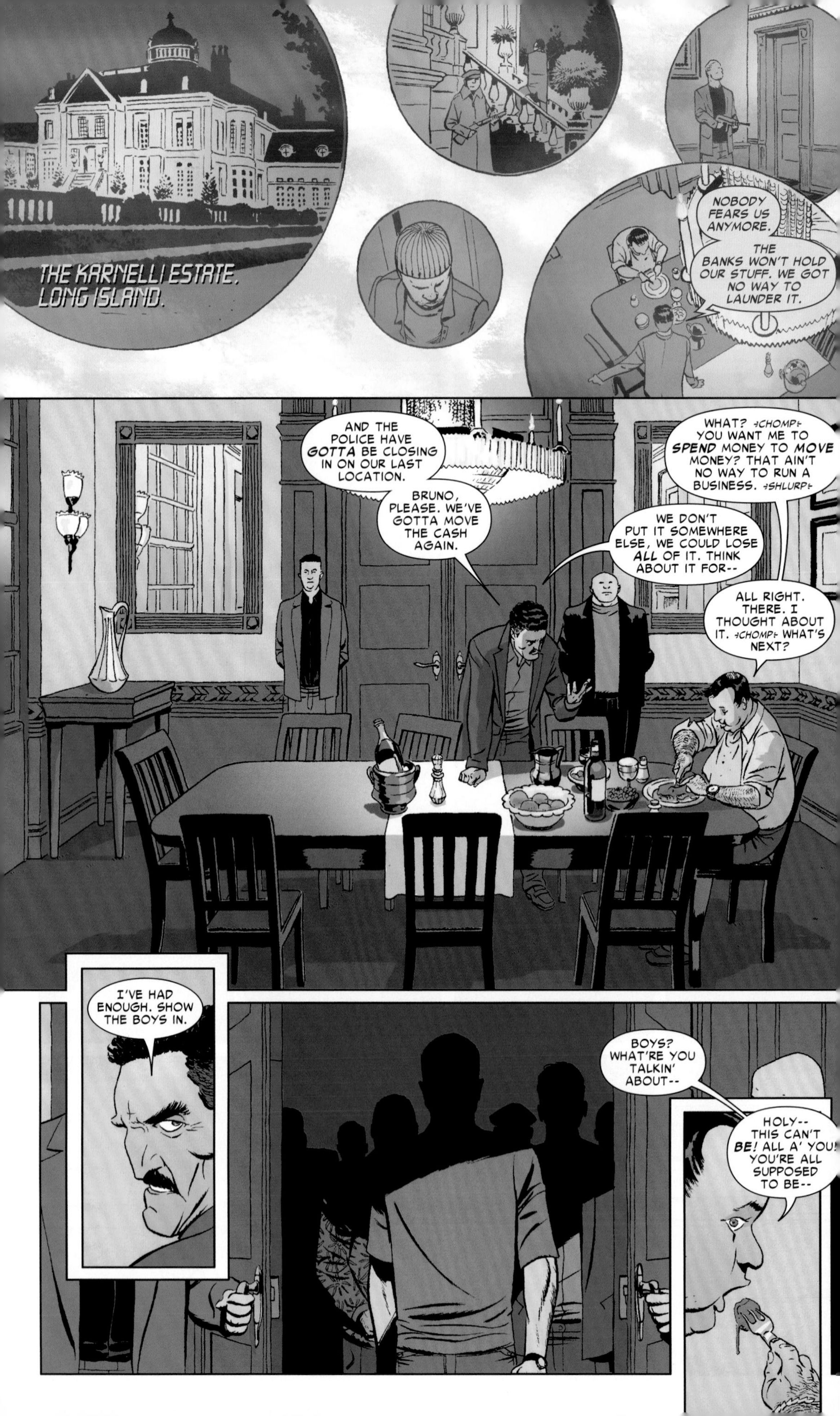
THE KARNELLI ESTATE. LONG ISLAND.
NOBODY FEARS US ANYMORE.
THE BANKS WON'T HOLD OUR STUFF. WE GOT NO WAY TO LAUNDER IT.
AND THE POLICE HAVE GOTTA BE CLOSING IN ON OUR LAST LOCATION.
BRUNO, PLEASE. WE'VE GOTTA MOVE THE CASH AGAIN.
WHAT? *CHOMP* YOU WANT ME TO SPEND MONEY TO MOVE MONEY? THAT AIN'T NO WAY TO RUN A BUSINESS. *SHLURP*
WE DON'T PUT IT SOMEWHERE ELSE, WE COULD LOSE ALL OF IT. THINK ABOUT IT FOR--
ALL RIGHT. THERE. I THOUGHT ABOUT IT. *CHOMP* WHAT'S NEXT?
I'VE HAD ENOUGH. SHOW THE BOYS IN.
BOYS? WHAT'RE YOU TALKIN' ABOUT--
HOLY-- THIS CAN'T BE! ALL A' YOU! YOU'RE ALL SUPPOSED TO BE--

DEAD? I WOULD BE.
IF I HADN'T BEEN SHOT UP WITH BLANKS AND BLOOD PACKS.
OR IF I DIDN'T HAVE AN ANTIDOTE IN THE HOUSE RED.
OR A TRAPDOOR UNDER MY CAR.
A REINFORCED COLLAR SAVED MY NECK.
LUCKY STIFF. I HAD TO PULL A "VAN GOGH."
NOT ME. I COULD AFFORD THE DELUXE PACKAGE: ROBOT DOUBLE.
ROBOT? NOT FOR A FIRE. I JUST HAD TO FIND SOMEONE AROUND MY HEIGHT.
MY BOYS AND I WERE WORRIED 'BOUT DNA. SO WE SPRUNG FOR--WHATTYA CALL IT?
CLONED BODY PARTS. THAT WAS ALL STAR WARS AND @#%*.
WHAT KINDA' MESSED UP AMILY REUNION IS THIS?!
LOOK, I DON'T CARE HOW MANY OF THESE MOOKS YOU PULL OUTTA THE GROUND!
FAR AS I CAN SEE, I STILL SIT AT THE HEAD A' THIS TABLE, AND I STILL CALL THE SHOTS!
THINK AGAIN, BABY BRUNO.

THUD

WHA?

WHAT IS THIS?
THUD

WHAT THE @#*% IS THIS?!

THUD

BUONA SERA, BRUNO. COME VA?
YOU LOOK LIKE YOU'VE SEEN A GHOST.
SILVERMANE!
DON MANFREDI! FORGIVE ME. BUT HOW IS THIS POSSIBLE?!
THE MAGGIA HAS EMPLOYED A SPECIALIST OVER THE YEARS.
SOMEONE WHO'S HELPED OUR BOYS PULL THESE "DISAPPEARING ACTS" WHEN THE HEAT WAS ON.
NOW, WITH HIS HELP, AND THAT OF OUR "DEARLY DEPARTED," WE'RE GONNA RETURN THE MAGGIA TO ITS FORMER GLORY.

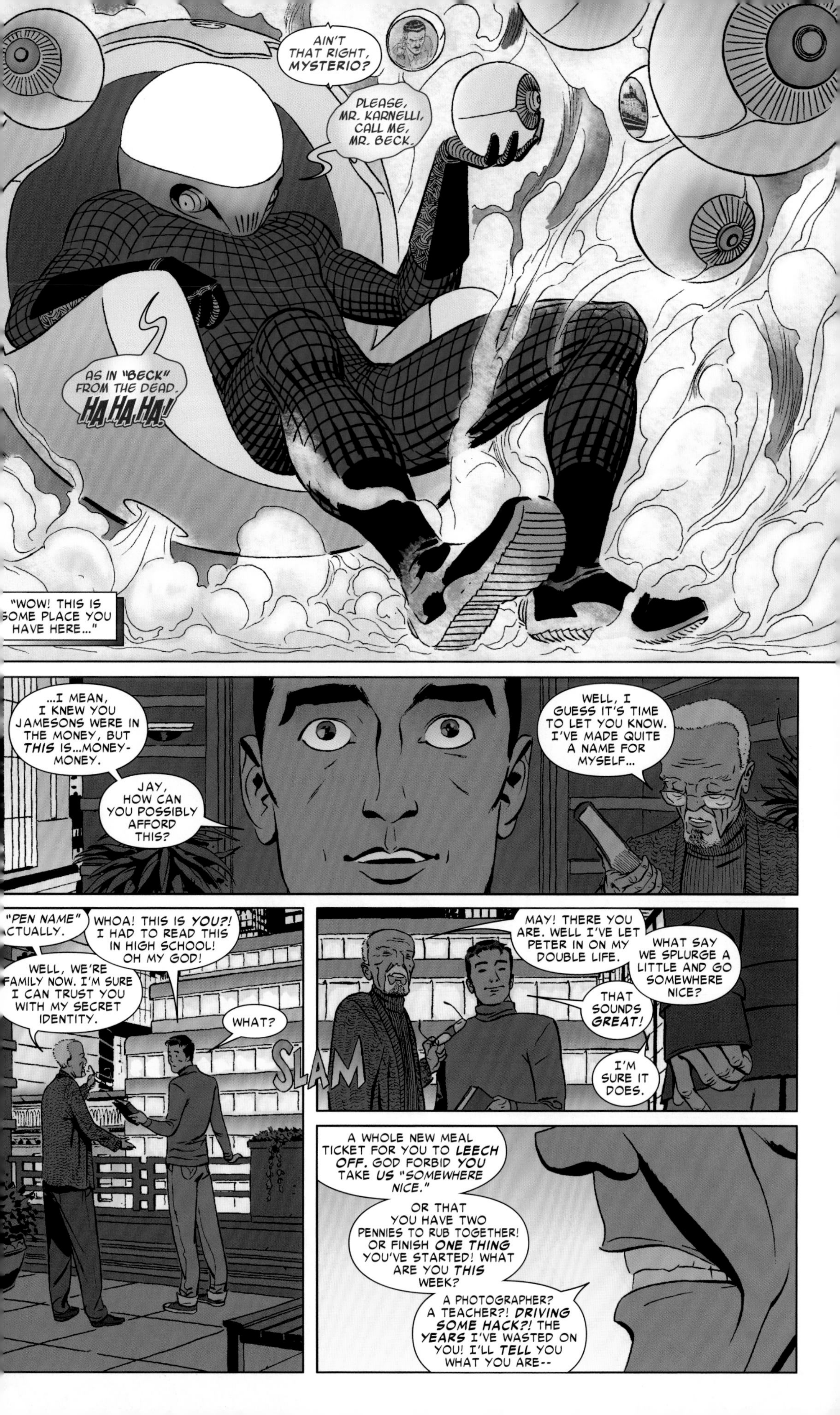
AIN'T THAT RIGHT, MYSTERIO?
PLEASE, MR. KARNELLI, CALL ME, MR. BECK.
AS IN "BECK" FROM THE DEAD. HA HA HA!
"WOW! THIS IS SOME PLACE YOU HAVE HERE..."
...I MEAN, I KNEW YOU JAMESONS WERE IN THE MONEY, BUT THIS IS...MONEY-MONEY.
JAY, HOW CAN YOU POSSIBLY AFFORD THIS?
WELL, I GUESS IT'S TIME TO LET YOU KNOW. I'VE MADE QUITE A NAME FOR MYSELF...
"PEN NAME" ACTUALLY.
WHOA! THIS IS YOU?! I HAD TO READ THIS IN HIGH SCHOOL! OH MY GOD!
WELL, WE'RE FAMILY NOW. I'M SURE I CAN TRUST YOU WITH MY SECRET IDENTITY.
WHAT?
SLAM
MAY! THERE YOU ARE. WELL I'VE LET PETER IN ON MY DOUBLE LIFE.
WHAT SAY WE SPLURGE A LITTLE AND GO SOMEWHERE NICE?
THAT SOUNDS GREAT!
I'M SURE IT DOES.
A WHOLE NEW MEAL TICKET FOR YOU TO LEECH OFF. GOD FORBID YOU TAKE US "SOMEWHERE NICE."
OR THAT YOU HAVE TWO PENNIES TO RUB TOGETHER! OR FINISH ONE THING YOU'VE STARTED! WHAT ARE YOU THIS WEEK?
A PHOTOGRAPHER? A TEACHER?! DRIVING SOME HACK?! THE YEARS I'VE WASTED ON YOU! I'LL TELL YOU WHAT YOU ARE--

ONE DAMN BIG DISAPPOINTMENT!

I-I HAVE TO GO.
PETER, WAIT. DON'T--
LEAVE HIM, JAY.

MAY? WHAT'S GOTTEN INTO YOU? I'VE NEVER SEEN YOU LIKE THIS.
SLAM
GET USED TO IT.

THE HONEYMOON'S OVER.

FIRE EXIT

MetLife
GOTTA CLEAR MY HEAD. THAT--THAT WAS PAINFUL. I'VE BEEN PUNCHED BY THE HULK, AND I'M TELLIN' YA...
...THAT WAS A HUNDRED TIMES WORSE. THAT WAS WAY OUTTA LINE. THAT WAS...
...TOTALLY TRUE. WHAT AM I DOING WITH MY LIFE?
COUPLE WEEKS AGO I BEAT DOC OCK IN A BATTLE OF THE MINDS. I OUT-BRAINBOXED OTTO OCTAVIUS!
ALL THAT POTENTIAL AND WHAT'VE I DONE WITH IT?
TALK ABOUT POWER AND RESPONSIBILITY!
A POLICE CONVOY?
THANK YOU, WORLD. I COULD USE A DISTRACTION ABOUT NOW!

HOPE NEW YORK'S FINEST DON'T MIND ME CUTTING IN.
'CAUSE, BOY, DO I WANT TO BEAT THE SNOT OUTTA SOMEBODY!
THIS IS CAPTAIN WATANABE. WE'VE GOT REPORTS OF MULTIPLE SHOTS FIRED IN THE MEATPACKING DISTRICT...

...IN A GANG WAR BETWEEN THE MAGGIA AND MR. NEGATIVE'S TONG. I WANT CONFIRMATION FROM THE OFFICER CALLING THIS IN!
IT'S OFFICER CARLIE COOPER, MA'AM.
COOPER? YOU'RE A BODY-BAGGER! WHAT'RE YOU DOING DOWN THERE?!

IT'S ALL RIGHT, CAPTAIN...

YOU TWO-BIT LOSERS THOUGHT YOU COULD TAKE FROM THE MAGGIA?!
NO MORE! WE'RE BACK, PUNKS! BACK FROM THE MOTHER-LOVIN' GRAVE!
...I WAS CHECKING OUT A LEAD.

NO KIDDIN'? WHY DON'T WE MAKE THAT A RETURN TRIP?!
HAMMERHEAD?! JOSEPH? WHAT IN GOD'S NAME ARE YOU DOING WITH THESE GUYS?!
YOU'RE MAGGIA!

BOSS?
THAT YOU?

IT WAS THE MONEY, CAPTAIN. IT SMELLED LIKE FISH.
OR RATHER SOME OF THE PRESERVATIVES USED TO PACK FISH.

A QUICK CHECK AND I FOUND THERE WERE ONLY THREE PACKING PLANTS IN THE CITY USING THOSE CHEMICALS--
COOPER, WE'RE ALMOST THERE! SIT TIGHT AND LAY LOW!
I'M A TRAINED OFFICER, CAPTAIN. I CAN LOOK AFTER MYSELF JUST FINE--

YOU SHOULDN'T BE HERE. WE'VE GOT TO GET YOU OUT OF HERE, NOW.
WHAT? WHO'S THERE? WHO'S--

AHH! NO...
...IT CAN'T BE. I SAW YOUR BODY. I WENT TO YOUR FUNERAL. YOU'RE-- YOU'RE--
NO, CARLIE. IT'S REALLY ME. I'M BACK.
DAD?!

THE AMAZING SPIDER-MAN #619

EVERYONE ON THE FORCE WILL TELL YOU: RAY COOPER WAS A GOOD COP.
PAST TENSE.
YOU CAN COUNT ON ME, GEORGE. IF THERE'S A LEAD HERE, I'LL FIND IT.
THANKS, RAY. THIS MAN WAS OUR TOP MAGGIA INFORMANT.
WE OWE IT TO HIM TO CATCH WHOEVER DID THIS.
DAD? YOU FORGOT YOUR LUNCH.

ENOUGH SHOP TALK. I'VE GOT A VISITOR. HEY, CARLIE-BEAR.
MS. COOPER.
HI, YURI. JEAN. CAPTAIN STACY.
HEH.
CAPTAIN?
JUST THINKING. KIDS ARE SO DIFFERENT. MY DAUGHTER'S HER AGE. SHE'LL DROP BY THE STATION, BUT...

"...I CAN'T IMAGINE HER EVER SETTING FOOT IN THE MORGUE."
MMPH. THANKS.
HEY, IS THIS A SPIDER-MAN CASE?
DID THIS GUY GET HIS INSIDES TURNED INTO SAND OR ELECTRICITY OR SOMETHING?

NOPE. THIS WAS A MOB SLAYING.
OH.
DON'T BE LIKE THAT. THIS'S RIVETING STUFF.
DAAAD, STOP BEING WEIRD.
NAME: LOU COSSI

HONEY, WHERE YOU SEE A BODY, I HEAR A STORY.
HE'S TELLING IT TO ME RIGHT NOW. A JUICY ONE. A CRIME STORY.
AS A FORENSIC SCIENTIST, I'M ONE OF THE FEW WHO CAN HEAR IT.
AND TRUST ME, CARLIE, DEAD MEN...

"...TELL THE BEST STORIES."
YES, CARLIE-BEAR. I'M ALIVE. HONEST.
BUT YOU--YOU WERE DRIVING. YOU HAD TOO MUCH TO DRINK. THERE WAS AN ACCIDENT--
I COULDN'T GET TO THE HOSPITAL IN TIME. I NEVER GOT TO SAY--
THE DOCTOR, HE PRONOUNCED YOU--
IT WAS SPECIAL EFFECTS, HONEY. THE BEST. GOOD ENOUGH TO FOOL ANYONE... EXCEPT A MEDICAL EXAMINER.
THE MAGGIA NEEDED ME TO PULL ALL THIS OFF. SOMEONE WHO KNEW THE SYSTEM, WHO COULD FAKE THE RECORDS AND--
NO! I DON'T BELIEVE YOU! YOU WOULD NEVER--
MY FATHER WOULD NEVER BE A PART OF ANYTHING LIKE THAT! HE WAS A--
NEEEEEOOOOOOEEEE
THE COPS!
I CALLED THEM IN. I--
LOOK, CARLIE, I CAN EXPLAIN EVERYTHING...
TONY'S
BUT WE CAN'T STAY HERE.

MYSTERIOSO

RE-APPEARING ACT PART 2

HAMMERHEAD?! SNAP OUT OF IT!
I DUNNO... THIS ISN'T RIGHT. THIS'S ALL...
AFTER ALL I'VE DONE FOR YOU! YOU SELL YOUR LOYALTY TO OUTSIDERS?
YOU TURN ON FAMILY?! IS THIS HOW YOU RESPECT ME, JOSEPH?!

STOP IT! ALL OF YOU--
--GET OUTTA MY HEAD!

WHOA! COMMON SENSE TINGLING!
SOMETHING TELLS ME I'M AT THE RIGHT PLACE.

HEY, PLUMB-SKULL! WHERE DO YOU THINK YOU'RE GOING?
PFT

TEP

THERE, THAT SHOULD MAKE SURE I DON'T LOSE YOU WHILE I--
HOLD IT RIGHT THERE, SPIDER-MAN.

FOR THE LUVVA--LOOK, AN WE DO THE WHOLE "*TRY TO ARREST SPIDEY*" THING SOME OTHER TIME? I GOTTA GO AFTER THE BAD GUY.
NO, YOU DON'T. YOU GOT A SPIDER-TRACER ON HIM. CATCH HIM ***LATER***. RIGHT NOW...
...I'VE GOT A DOZEN OFFICERS ABOUT TO WALK INTO A FIREFIGHT AND ONE ALREADY ON THE SCENE. WE COULD REALLY USE YOUR HELP.
SAY, I KNOW YOU!
CAPTAIN YURI WATANABE. WE'VE MET.

SO CAP, WHERE'S ALL THIS SPIDEY-TRUST COMING FROM? NOT THAT I MIND.
I CAME UP THROUGH THE RANKS WITH JEAN DeWOLFF. SHE SPOKE WELL OF YOU.
A LOT.

OH, THAT DOES IT. YOU'RE GETTING A FRIEND REQUEST. YOU ON FACEBOOK OR MYSPACE?
UM... MYSPACE.
ARE YOU ***SEEING*** THIS?!

"THAT'S SILVERMANE...

"THERE'S VINCENZO KARNELLI, PAULO MUNOZ...

"...AND A DOZEN MAGGIA FOOTSOLDIERS WHO ARE SUPPOSED TO BE *DEAD!*

"AND ALL THE MEN FROM MR. NEGATIVE'S TONG...

"...THEY'RE SHAKING OFF GUNSHOT WOUNDS?!"

UNDEAD MOBSTERS? MASKED MEN WHO WON'T DIE?! THIS'S *INSANE!*
WELCOME TO *MY* WORLD. JUST ANOTHER DAY IN THE FRIENDLY NEIGHBORHOOD.
ALL RIGHT! EVERYONE, **FREEZE!**
THIS'S THE NYPD! *YOU'RE ALL UNDER ARREST!*
NY PD

WHAT NOW, BOSS?
CHANGE OF PLANS, BOYS. IF NEGATIVE'S FREAKS CAN'T BE KILLED...
...CRIPPLE 'EM INSTEAD!
HOW? THEY KEEP GETTING BACK ON THEIR FEET!
THAT'S IT RIGHT THERE, JIMMY.
IT'S LIKE THE SAME WAY YOU TAKE ON AN ARMORED CAR...
...SHOOT OUT THE TIRES!
BLOW OFF THEIR FEET AND THEY WON'T HAVE NOTHING TO STAND ON! ALL A' YOU, GO FOR THEIR LEGS!
GOOD ADVICE. ME, ON THE OTHER HAND...
UH?
...I GO FOR THE HEADSHOT. WORKS EVERY TIME.
ESPECIALLY ON GUYS IN BATTLE SUITS WITH EXPOSED CHINS. WHAT'S UP WITH THAT?
D'YOU TELL THE GUY AT THE ARMOR STORE, "GIVE ME PROTECTION EVERYWHERE BUT MY FACE"?
POW

ARHH!
BOOM
BOOM
BOOM
DON'T REALLY SEE THE POINT A' THIS.
THEY'RE JUST GONNA GROW THE DAMN THINGS BACK.
YEAH? AND BY THE TIME THEY'VE DONE THAT, WE'LL BE LONG GONE.
THE COPS'LL HAVE ROUNDED 'EM UP. TOSSED 'EM IN CELLS.
AAAND?
GNHH...
AND THEY'LL BE OUT OF OUR HAIR. NOT BAD. THAT SILVERMANE'S A SMART GUY.
YEAH. A LOT BETTER THAN BABY BRUNO, THAT'S FOR SURE!
I KNEW EVERYTHING WOULD WORK OUT ONCE I GOT CONTROL OF THE MAGGIA...
...EVEN IF IT IS REMOTE CONTROL. HEY, BECK...

...HOW'S OUR "PUPPET DICTATOR" HOLDING UP? CAN'T HAVE YOUR SILVERMANE ROBOT BREAKING DOWN ON ME.
SURE, IT'S GOOD AGAINST THE COPS AND MR. NEGATIVE'S BOYS. BUT WHAT ABOUT SPIDER-MAN?
MR. KARNELLI, I'M MYSTERIO. I ALWAYS PLAN FOR SPIDER-MAN.
LISTEN UP, CREW! PLACES FOR GAG SEVENTEEN.
LOU, YOU'RE TAKING POINT ON THIS ONE.
HEY!
I'VE GOT THE WALL-CRAWLER IN POSITION.
PUTTING HIM INTO PLAY. NOW!
WE ONLY GET ONE TAKE AT THIS. MAKE IT COUNT!
AH!

BRRRRTTTTT
FIRING ON ME? REALLY?
THIS'S THE THANKS I GET...
...FOR SAVING YOU MAGGIA GUYS THE OTHER DAY.
THOUGHT YOU WERE ON OUR SIDE!

POK
NAH. YOU'RE ALL JUST CROOKS TO ME. AND I'M HERE TO STOP A GANG WAR.
THAT MEANS YOU'RE ALL GOING DOWN!

WHAT?!

NYPD

WAIT! I DIDN'T--

KRAK

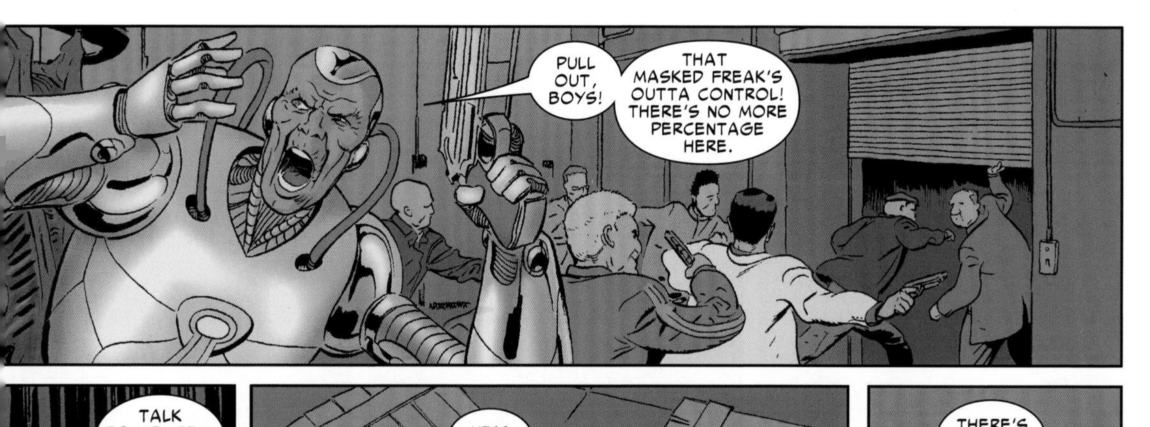
PULL OUT, BOYS!
THAT MASKED FREAK'S OUTTA CONTROL! THERE'S NO MORE PERCENTAGE HERE.

TALK TO ME. TELL ME HOW HE'S--
HE'S DEAD.
NO! HE CAN'T BE.
I'VE BEEN DOING THIS FOR YEARS. I KNOW HOW HARD TO HIT A NORMAL GUY...

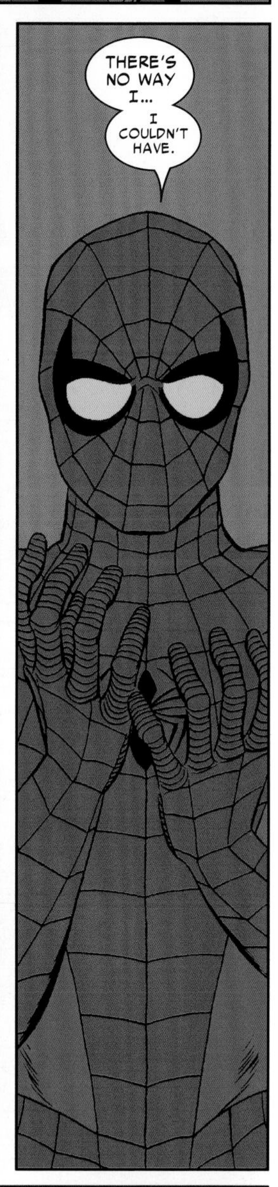
THERE'S NO WAY I...
I COULDN'T HAVE.

WHAT'RE YOU STANDING AROUND FOR?!
I WANT NEGATIVE'S MEN LOCKED UP *NOW!*
NYPD
CAPTAIN, WHAT ABOUT *HIM?*

WHAT? SPIDER-MAN? HE'S TOO FAST.
YOU'D NEVER BE ABLE TO CATCH HIM. AND BESIDES...
...HE'S ALREADY OFF CHASING AFTER THOSE MOB GUYS.

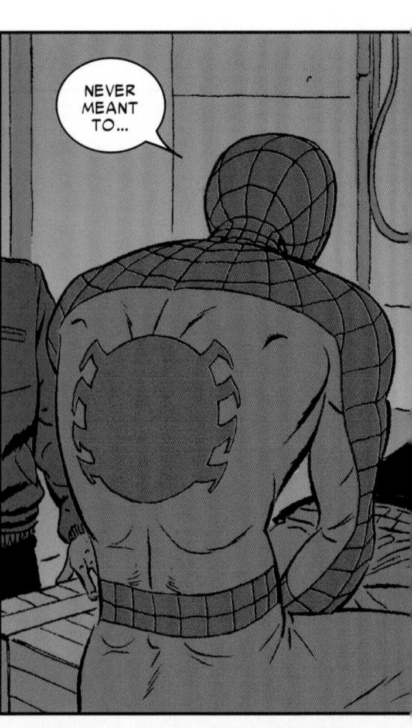
NEVER MEANT TO...

I SAID, HE'S TOO FAST. AND HE'S ***ALREADY OFF*** CHASING AFTER THOSE MOB GUYS.

UM... YEAH. RIGHT.

CAPTAIN! YOU CAN'T BE SERIOUS HERE! A BLUE WALL A' SILENCE IS ONE THING--
--A ***RED AND BLUE*** WALL OF SILENCE IS SOMETHING ELSE! THE MAN'S A VIGILANTE ***AND*** A KILLER!
NO, HE'S NOT. NOT EVEN ON HIS WORST DAY.
BUT CAPTAIN! LOOK!
I DON'T CARE. I'VE SEEN A ***LOT*** OF THINGS TONIGHT I CAN'T BELIEVE. THIS? THIS I ***WON'T*** BELIEVE.

BLOCK OFF THE AREA. NOBODY TOUCH ANYTHING TILL THE C.S.I.S GET HERE. AND SOMEBODY FIND ME CARLIE COOPER.
SHE'S AROUND HERE SOMEWHERE. WE WERE IN CONTACT TILL HER MIKE CUT OUT.
POLIC
I DIDN'T WANT TO SPRING ALL OF THIS ON YOU AT ONCE.
BUT I HAD TO WARN YOU BEFORE THIS BECAME A CRIME SCENE...
DAD, WAIT.

WATANABE'S LOOKING FOR ME. IF SHE FINDS YOU...
MPIA GA
212-

POLIC

CAPTAIN?
THERE YOU ARE, COOPER. I KNOW I CHEWED YOU OFF A PIECE EARLIER. BUT I'M GLAD YOU'RE HERE NOW.
I NEED YOU TO BABY-SIT A BODY FROM ON-SITE ALL THE WAY TO THE MORGUE.
SOMETHING HINKY'S GOING ON, AND I WANT TO GET TO THE BOTTOM OF IT.
WHO'S THE VIC?

NOT IMPORTANT. IT'S THE PERP. DOZEN EYEWITNESSES, MYSELF INCLUDED, MAKE SPIDEY FOR THIS ONE.
PROVE ME WRONG, COOPER. LAST THING THIS DEPARTMENT NEEDS IS ANOTHER FALSE CHARGE AGAINST SPIDER-MAN.

OH, MY... CAPTAIN, I KNOW THIS MAN. I'VE SEEN THIS CORPSE YEARS AGO...
...DOWN IN THE MORGUE. THIS IS--

--UN-FRICKIN' BELIEVABLE.

LET ME GET THIS STRAIGHT. WHILE I WAS OFF ON MY HONEYMOON...

YOU, AND MY GOOD-FOR-NOTHING RELATIONS, MOVE INTO MY HOUSE IN QUEENS...

...AND YOU TORCH IT?!

IT WASN'T OUR FAULT, AUNT MAY, THERE WAS THIS SUPER VILLAIN*, HE BROKE IN AND--
SELL IT TO SOMEONE WHO GIVES A DAMN. LOOK AT THIS PLACE!
MAY, PLEASE. I'M SORRY. I ONLY CAME HERE BECAUSE I HAD NOWHERE ELSE TO GO.
I SWEAR, HARRY OSBORN, I'M GOING TO SUE YOUR PAMPERED, TRUST FUND BUTT FOR EVERYTHING YOU'VE GOT.
TELL ME HOW THAT'S MY PROBLEM? ALL OF YOU, END OF THE WEEK, YOU'RE OUT!
BUT WHERE WILL WE--?
*ASM #608 - #610--STEVE.

THERE'S ALWAYS PLENTY OF COTS DOWN AT THE SHELTER.

SLAM
HARRY? IS SHE SERIOUS? YOU EVAH SEE HER LIKE THIS?
NEVER, AMES. NOT ONCE.

TRUST ME, YOU HAVE YET TO SEE THE FULL EXTENT OF MY DARK SIDE.

ARGHH!
THIS IS BUT A TASTE OF THE PAIN I CAN INFLICT ON YOU, HAMMERHEAD.
IT'S AN OBEDIENCE DEVICE I HAD DR. TRAMMA PLACE INSIDE YOUR REBUILT FRAME.
I HOPE IT HELPS YOU CLARIFY WHERE YOUR LOYALTIES SHOULD LIE.

YEAH, THINGS ARE CLEAR NOW. PAINFULLY CLEAR.
GOOD. NOW TO THE MATTER AT HAND. WE SHOULD-- WAIT! YOU'VE BEEN MARKED BY THE SPIDER.

KREK

AH, SPIDER-MAN. THE ITCH THAT REFUSES TO BE SCRATCHED TO DEATH

FORTUNATELY, I ALREADY POSSESS THE REMEDY.
"FOR SOME PEOPLE, TAKING A LIFE IS SO EASY..."

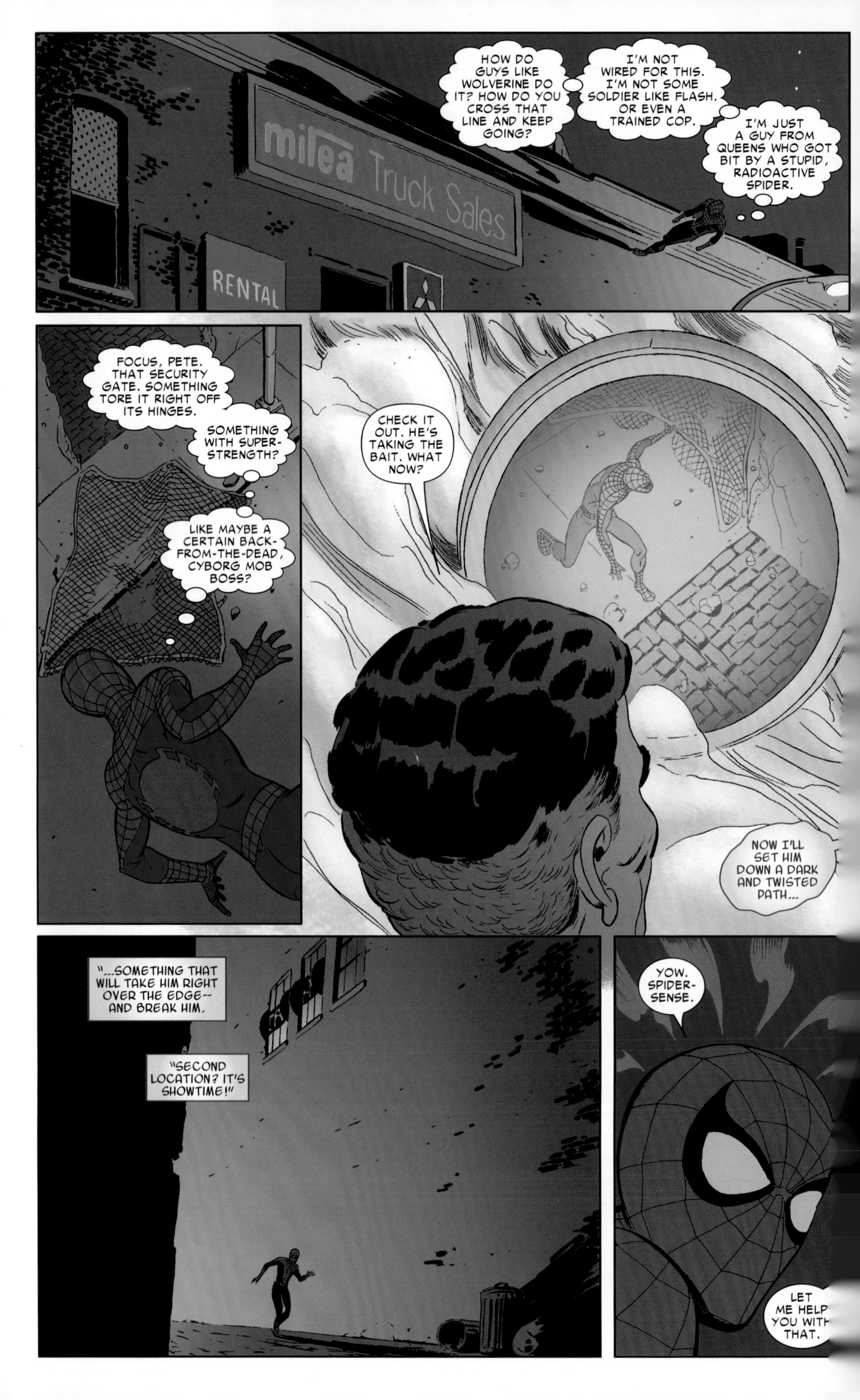
milea Truck Sales
RENTAL
HOW DO GUYS LIKE WOLVERINE DO IT? HOW DO YOU CROSS THAT LINE AND KEEP GOING?
I'M NOT WIRED FOR THIS. I'M NOT SOME SOLDIER LIKE FLASH. OR EVEN A TRAINED COP.
I'M JUST A GUY FROM QUEENS WHO GOT BIT BY A STUPID, RADIOACTIVE SPIDER.
FOCUS, PETE. THAT SECURITY GATE. SOMETHING TORE IT RIGHT OFF ITS HINGES.
SOMETHING WITH SUPER-STRENGTH?
LIKE MAYBE A CERTAIN BACK-FROM-THE-DEAD, CYBORG MOB BOSS?
CHECK IT OUT. HE'S TAKING THE BAIT. WHAT NOW?
NOW I'LL SET HIM DOWN A DARK AND TWISTED PATH...
"...SOMETHING THAT WILL TAKE HIM RIGHT OVER THE EDGE-- AND BREAK HIM.
"SECOND LOCATION? IT'S SHOWTIME!"
YOW. SPIDER-SENSE.
LET ME HELP YOU WITH THAT.

I CAN PUT AN END TO THAT ANNOYING SPIDER-SENSE ONCE AND FOR ALL.
BOYS, LET'S SHOW THIS WEB-HEADED FREAK WHAT HAPPENS WHEN YOU MESS WITH THE MAGGIA.
THE BIG MAN?!
FRANKY, LIGHT THIS LOSER UP!
BRTTTTTTT
C'MON! REALLY? IT'S GONNA TAKE MORE THAN THAT MASK AND A GOOFY HAT...
THWP
...TO MAKE ME BUY THAT THE BIG MAN'S BACK. TREAT ME WITH A LITTLE RESPECT HERE.
URRH!
FRANKY! LET GO OF THE--!!
KPOW KPOW
NO!
BLAM BLAM
RTT
BL

NOT AGAIN!
THEY'RE ALL--
⇟KAFF⇞ ⇟KOFF⇞

YOU! YOU'RE STILL ALIVE!
TELL ME! WHAT'S GOING ON!
⇟KAFF⇞

I DON'T KNOW WHAT YOU'RE PLAYING AT, BUT YOU ARE NOT FREDERICK FOSWELL! I SAW HIM DIE...
FOSWELL WAS NEVER THE BIG MAN. ⇟KOFF⇞-- HE WAS A FRONT.
SOMEONE THAT COULD PROVIDE--⇟KAFF⇞-- ME WITH AN ALIBI...

...BUT IT WAS ME, SON. ⇟KOFF⇞ IT WAS ALWAYS ME.
CAPTAIN STACY?!

AHH!
NO! NO! NO!

NOT BUYING IT!
NOT FOR ONE SECOND!
STOP IT!

GEORGE TACY? THE BIG MAN? A DIRTY COP WORKING FOR THE MAGGIA?
AND WITH ALL THE OTHER IMPOSSIBLE THINGS THAT'VE HAPPENED TODAY?
YOU JUST TIPPED YOUR HAND! I KNOW YOU'RE BEHIND THIS NOW!

PLEASE! THIS WASN'T MY IDEA! I--
SHUT UP! I'M NOT TALKING TO YOU!
I'M TALKING TO THE GUY WHO'S FILMING, WATCHING, AND GETTING HIS JOLLIES FROM EVERY MINUTE OF THIS.
YOU WENT TOO FAR THIS TIME, MYSTERIO! NOW IT'S PERSONAL!
BECK?
THIS DOESN'T CHANGE A THING. HE'S RILED. HE'S ANGRY. HE'LL BE OFF HIS GAME.
I AM STILL IN CONTROL.

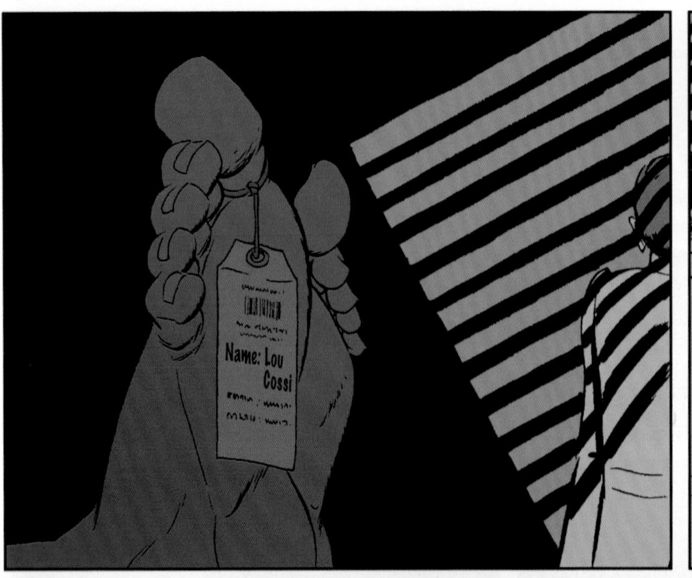
Name: Lou Cossi

CARLIE.
HEY, SPIDEY.
I HAVE TO KNOW. WHAT DID THE AUTOPSY SHOW? DID I KILL THAT MAN?
I DIDN'T PERFORM AN AUTOPSY. IF I HAD...THAT WOULD'VE KILLED HIM.
WHAT?

HE ISN'T DEAD. EVEN NOW. HE'S BEEN GIVEN A DRUG THAT MAKES IT LOOK LIKE--
I COULD'VE KILLED HIM. THAT'S HOW THEY GOT MY FATHER INVOLVED IN THIS.
YOUR FATHER?

IT STARTED OFF WITH BLOOD ON HIS HANDS, THEN IT MOVED ON TO...OTHER THINGS.
HE FAKED HIS OWN DEATH AS WELL. HE CAME BACK TO WARN ME SO IT WOULDN'T HAPPEN TO ME TOO.
WHAT SHOULD I DO?
FOR STARTERS, PLAY SMART. THIS GUY, HE MIGHT NOT EVEN BE YOUR DAD...

...BUT WHOEVER HE IS, HE'S OUR BIGGEST LINK TO WHAT'S GOING ON. SO IF HE GETS IN TOUCH WITH YOU AGAIN....
...I'M GONNA NEED A FAVOR. A BIG ONE.
"THEY KEEP TRACKIN' US DOWN. KNOW HOW...?"

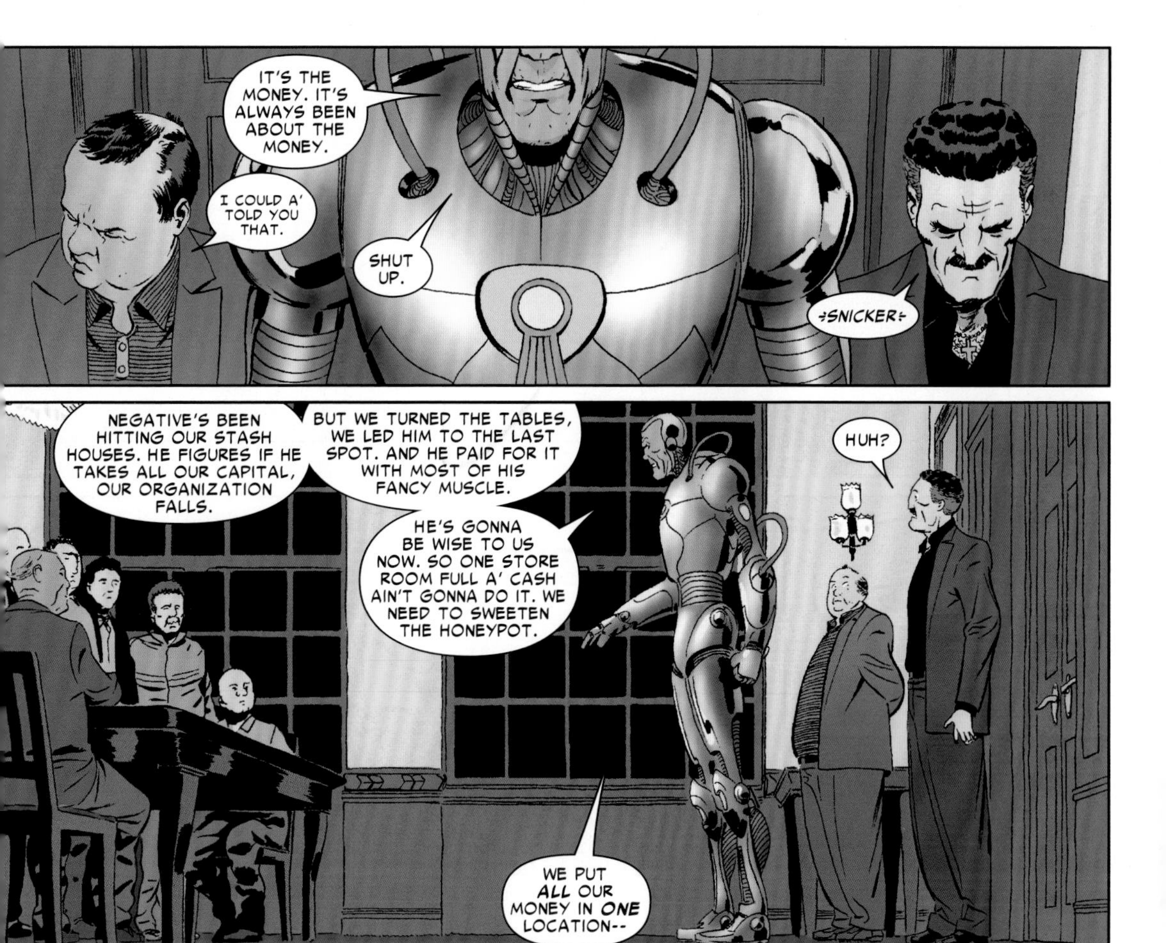
IT'S THE MONEY. IT'S ALWAYS BEEN ABOUT THE MONEY.
I COULD A' TOLD YOU THAT.
SHUT UP.
SNICKER
NEGATIVE'S BEEN HITTING OUR STASH HOUSES. HE FIGURES IF HE TAKES ALL OUR CAPITAL, OUR ORGANIZATION FALLS.
BUT WE TURNED THE TABLES, WE LED HIM TO THE LAST SPOT. AND HE PAID FOR IT WITH MOST OF HIS FANCY MUSCLE.
HE'S GONNA BE WISE TO US NOW. SO ONE STORE ROOM FULL A' CASH AIN'T GONNA DO IT. WE NEED TO SWEETEN THE HONEYPOT.
HUH?
WE PUT **ALL** OUR MONEY IN **ONE** LOCATION--

THAT'S **NOT** THE PLAN!

QUIET! YOUR DON IS TALKING.

YOU! YOU'RE **NOT** THE DON OF THIS FAMILY! YOU'RE JUST--

GAKK

SNAP
HEY! HE KILLED CARMINE!
GOTCHA.
THIS'S JUST ANOTHER FAKE DEATH. HE'S PERFECTLY FINE.
HA. GOOD ONE, BOSS. YOU REALLY HAD US.
HA HA HA HA HA HA HA
NAH. I'M JUST MESSIN' WIT YOU. HE'S DEAD!
BUT MAYBE NO YOU'LL AL REMEMBER

...WHO REALLY PULLS ALL THE STRINGS AROUND HERE!

THE AMAZING SPIDER-MAN #620

COVER ARTWORK

KNOW WHAT I LIKE ABOUT ORGANIZED CRIME? IT'S VERY MUCH A CASH-IN-HAND KIND OF BUSINESS.
FROM PROTECTION...
CHEESE
Dairy
OPEN

...TO PROSTITUTION...

...TO NARCOTICS.

...IT'S ALL ABOUT THE MONEY.
SO YOU HAVE TO ASK YOURSELF, WHERE DOES IT ALL GO?

WELL, IN THE CASE OF THE MAGGIA CRIME FAMILY, IT'S JUST BEEN SITTING THERE.
FOR MONTHS, A RIVAL MOB BOSS, MR. NEGATIVE, HAS BEEN CHIPPING AWAY AT THEIR LEGITIMATE HOLDINGS...

...LEAVING THEM NO WAY TO LAUNDER ALL OF THEIR DIRTY SWAG.

FORCING THEM TO MOVE IT FROM ONE STASH HOUSE TO THE NEXT...
...TILL TONIGHT, WHERE IT ALL WINDS UP HERE...

...AT THE OLD EMPYREAN OPERA HOUSE.
EMPYREAN THEATER

THE MAGGIA THINKS WE'RE DOING THIS TO BAIT NEGATIVE INTO A TRAP.
THAT'S NOT IT AT ALL. THAT'S MISDIRECTION. WITH ME IT'S ALWAYS ABOUT MISDIRECTION.

MYSTERIOSO
PART 3
SMOKE & MIRRORS
STORY DAN SLOTT
ART MARCOS MARTIN PAGES 1-2 13-22
JAVIER PULIDO PAGES 3-12
COLORS JAVIER RODRÍGUEZ
LETTERS JOE CARAMAGNA
ASST. EDITOR TOM BRENNAN
DIVA STEPHEN WACKER
EXECUTIVE EDITOR TOM BREVOORT
EDITOR-IN-CHIEF JOE QUESADA
PUBLISHER DAN BUCKLEY
EXECUTIVE PRODUCER ALAN FINE
WEBHEADS GALE, KELLY, SLOTT, VAN LENTE, WAID & WELLS
THEY CALL ME QUENTIN BECK, THE ONE AND ONLY MYSTERIO.
OR MAYBE THE REAL BECK IS DEAD? I WOULDN'T TRUST ME ON THIS. I LIE ABOUT EVERYTHING.
...SO WITH THE FIRST HIT, THEY'RE GONNA SEE MY BLOOD N' GUTS GOIN' EVERYWHERE?
YEAH. THAT SHOULD GIVE YOU A SECOND TO GET THE DROP ON 'EM.
BOSS, I GOTTA ASK...
WHY'RE WE TAKING THE TIME TO RIG THESE GUYS FOR FAKE DEATHS WHEN...
...WHEN THEY'RE ALL GOING TO DIE ANYWAY?
BECAUSE IT'S BETTER TO HAVE THE MARKS THINK THAT THEY'RE PLAYERS...

"...INSTEAD OF THE ONES GETTING *PLAYED.*"
THANKS FOR MEETING ME HERE ON SUCH SHORT--
I'M NOT FALLING FOR THIS.

CARLIE-BEAR?
STOP SAYING THAT. DO I LOOK *STUPID* TO YOU? MY LATE FATHER, THE MAN I MODELED MY LIFE AFTER...
...SHOWS UP TO TELL ME THAT EVERYTHING I KNOW IS A LIE.

THAT HE WAS A DIRTY COP--WORKING WITH MYSTERIO--TO FAKE THE DEATHS OF KEY MEMBERS OF THE MOB?
YOU SAY THAT, AND ALL I HEAR IS "MYSTERIO," "FAKE," AND "DEATH." PROVE TO ME YOU'RE *RAY COOPER! RIGHT NOW!*
IT WAS BECAUSE OF YOUR MOM, HONEY. YOU REMEMBER? SHE'D GOTTEN SO ILL.
A COP'S SALARY, WHAT INSURANCE WE HAD, THEY COULDN'T PAY FOR ALL HER TREATMENTS. AND WHEN SHE PASSED AWAY...
...I FELT OUR FAMILY DIDN'T OWE THE SYSTEM ANY LOYALTY. IF ANYTHING, I WAS GOING TO MAKE IT WORK FOR US!

THAT'S WHY I CAME BACK. MYSTERIO'S BIG PAYDAY IS COMING, AND THIS IS WHEN I GET MY CUT.
ENOUGH TO BUY THIS FAMILY A FUTURE WE DESERVE! YOU AND ME.

BUT IF YOU'D RATHER NOT...
DAD!

WAIT! DON'T GO, OKAY?

EASY, CARLIE-BEAR. THIS'LL WORK, YOU'LL SEE. I WON'T BE LONG.
YOU BETTER NOT. THERE'S NO WAY I'M LOSING YOU AGAIN.

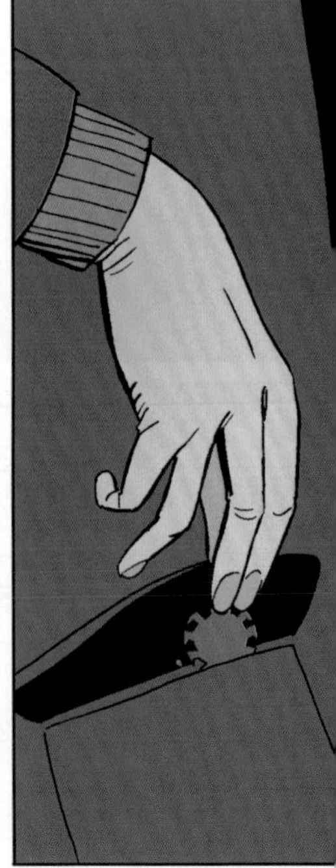

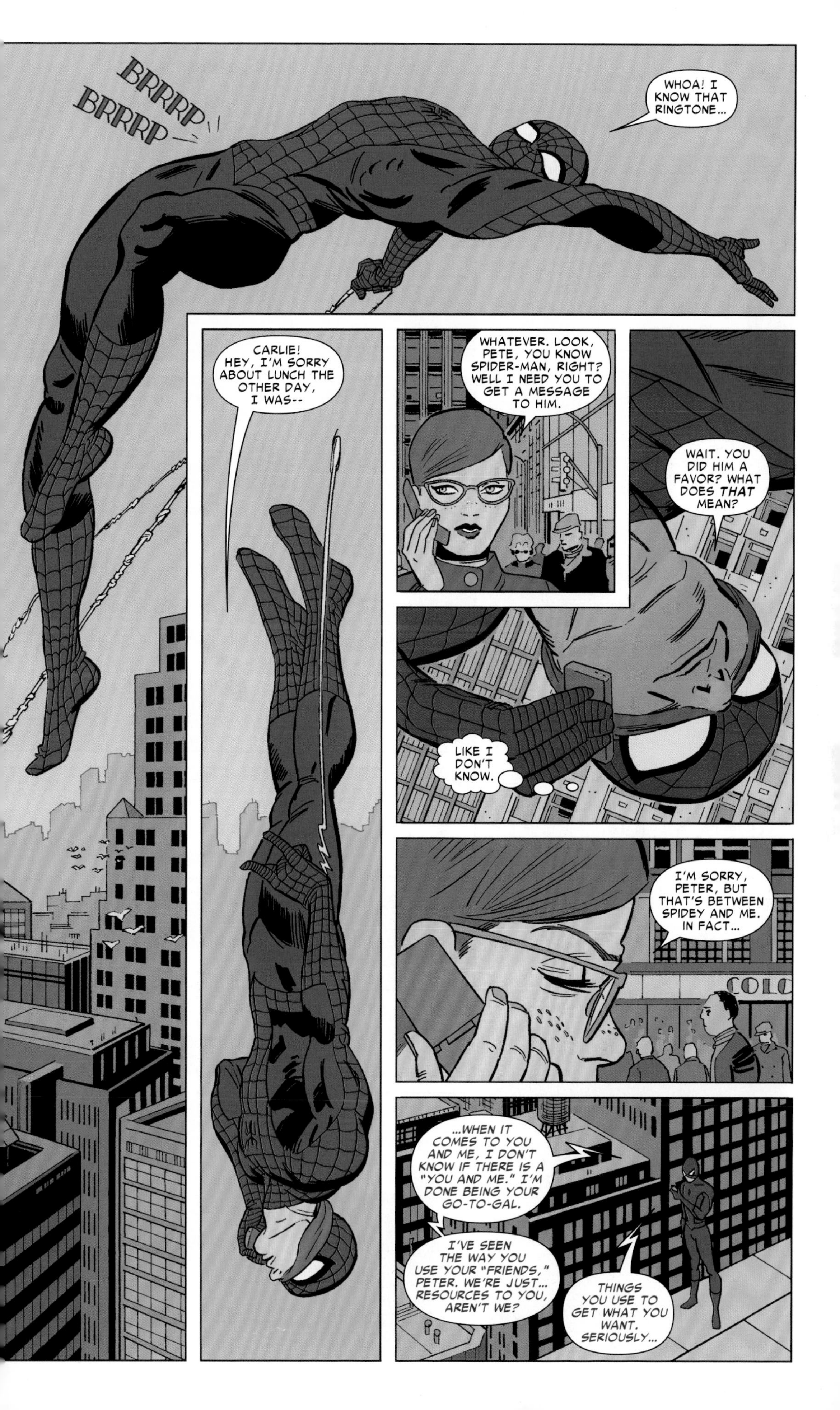

BRRRRP BRRRRP
WHOA! I KNOW THAT RINGTONE...
CARLIE! HEY, I'M SORRY ABOUT LUNCH THE OTHER DAY, I WAS--
WHATEVER. LOOK, PETE, YOU KNOW SPIDER-MAN, RIGHT? WELL I NEED YOU TO GET A MESSAGE TO HIM.
WAIT. YOU DID HIM A FAVOR? WHAT DOES THAT MEAN?
LIKE I DON'T KNOW.
I'M SORRY, PETER, BUT THAT'S BETWEEN SPIDEY AND ME. IN FACT...
...WHEN IT COMES TO YOU AND ME, I DON'T KNOW IF THERE IS A "YOU AND ME." I'M DONE BEING YOUR GO-TO-GAL.
I'VE SEEN THE WAY YOU USE YOUR "FRIENDS," PETER. WE'RE JUST... RESOURCES TO YOU, AREN'T WE?
THINGS YOU USE TO GET WHAT YOU WANT. SERIOUSLY...

"...WHO TREATS PEOPLE LIKE THAT?"
WHAT IS HAMMERHEAD'S STATUS, DR. TRAMMA?
YOU USED HIS OBEDIENCE PROTOCOLS A LITTLE TOO VIGOROUSLY, MR. NEGATIVE. HIS NERVOUS SYSTEM'S FRIED.
I WANT HIM READY FOR THE FINAL ASSAULT.
THIS ISN'T LENSCRAFTERS. I'M REBUILDING NEURAL PATHWAYS. HE'LL BE READY WHEN HE'S READY.
VERY WELL. MEN...
...LOAD UP THE CANISTERS OF DEVIL'S BREATH. THEY SHOULD KEEP SPIDER-MAN FROM INTERFERING IN THESE AFFAIRS.
IF WHAT YOU SAY IS TRUE, IF SILVERMANE HAS RETURNED, I WANT NOTHING STANDING IN THE WAY BETWEEN HIM...
...AND MY WELL DESERVED VENGEANCE.*
*SEE MR. NEGATIVE #1-#3--STEVE.
SIR, IT'S OUR INFORMANT AT THE POLICE PRECINCT. ON THE SECURE LINE.
HE'S LEARNED THE LOCATION OF THE MAGGIA'S STASH HOUSE.
WHERE IS IT, OFFICER?
YO! YOU KNOW THE DRILL, FIRST YOU GOTTA PAY UP.
YOUR FEE IS BEING WIRED TO YOUR ANONYMOUS ACCOUNT. NOW OUT WITH IT.
THE OLD EMPYREAN THEATER THAT'S PRETTY CLOSE TO WHERE YOU ARE NOW, HUH?
CLICK
THE FINAL PIECE IS SET IN MOTION AND I'M GETTING PAID FOR IT.
CUT, PRINT, AND PUT THAT ON THE COMPILATION REEL. THAT'S A KEEPER!
VERY PROUD OF YOURSELF, AREN'T YOU?

CLAP
CLAP
AND OF YOU, MR. COOPER. YOU WEREN'T ACTUALLY COUNTING YOUR TAKE.
YOU WERE CHECKING FOR ANY OF MY BUGS, TRICKS, OR TRAPS, WEREN'T YOU?
WHEN DEALING WITH YOU...
...IT PAYS TO BE CAUTIOUS. OH, JUST SO YOU KNOW...
...IF ANYTHING SHOULD HAPPEN TO ME...
ZZIP
...A TIME SENSITIVE FILE GOES OUT TO A MAJOR NEWS SITE WITH DETAILS OF EVERY FAKE DEATH WE ENGINEERED.
I DOUBT YOUR CLIENTS WOULD BE HAPPY ABOUT THAT.
PLEASE, LIKE I'M THE KIND OF GUY WHO'D PULL A DOUBLE CROSS.
HERE YOU GO, BOSS. WE GOT THAT C-4 READY.
RIIIGHT. BEFORE I GO, TELL ME SOMETHING.
YOU WIPE OUT THE MAGGIA, PIN IT ON NEGATIVE, AND LEAVE WITH THE CASH. I GET THAT.
BUT RIGHT NOW, YOU CONTROL "SILVERMANE." YOU'RE RUNNING A CRIMINAL EMPIRE. WHY PLAY THE SHORT GAME?
TWO REASONS, RAY. ONE: PULLING OFF THE GAG. THAT'S MY RUSH, NOT THE DAY-TO-DAY STUFF.
AND TWO: THERE'S ONLY SO LONG YOU CAN KEEP A CON GOING BEFORE SOME RANDOM VARIABLE SHOWS UP AND RUINS EVERYTH--
BEEP BEEP
INTRUDER
SEE? HE'S EARLY. NOW HOW ON EARTH DID HE FIND THIS PLACE?
WELL, I KNOW A CUE TO LEAVE WHEN I HEAR ONE. G'LUCK WITH THIS, QUENTIN.
TEAMS, TO THE SOUTH ENTRANCE! WE HAVE A VISITOR! OPEN FIRE!

KEEP HIM BUSY TILL OUR "GUESTS" SHOW UP!
SPITT
SPITT
YOW! WELL EXCUSE ME FOR BARGING IN.
DIDN'T KNOW YOU WERE ENTERTAINING.

BLAMMM
BRRRRRT
BLAMMM
SPEAKING OF ENTERTAINING...
...I'M HAVING A HARD TIME FIGURING OUT WHAT'S *REAL* HERE AND WHAT'S FOR SHOW.

NOW MY SPIDER-SENSE SAYS THOSE *AREN'T* BLANKS!
BUT WHAT ABOUT YOU GUYS?

WITH MYSTERIO, YOU CAN NEVER TELL. ARE YOU MOBSTERS OR EXTRAS?
'CAUSE IF YOU'RE JUST HERE TO GET POINTS ON YOUR EQUITY CARDS, I CAN PULL MY--

ARGHH!
SPLURCH
HURHK!
SPLATT

EWW! REALLY?!
I KNOW IT'S FAKE, BUT STILL! YUCK, THAT'S GROSS!

YA GOT US.
IT WAS THE ENTRAILS, WASN'T IT? LI'L OVER THE TOP, RIGHT?

JUST GREAT. STAGE BLOOD OR NOT...
...THIS BETTER WASH OUT OF MY TIGHTS!

BRRRRRRTTT
BLAMMM
D'OH! WAS THAT A KIDNEY?
ICK! THAT'S JUST WRONG!
NO! NOT A LOOSE EYEBALL!
BLAMMM
I AM NOT GOOD WITH EYEBALLS!

THIS--THIS IS WHY I DON'T GO TO THE SAW MOVIES.
UGH. I'M GONNA BE SICK!

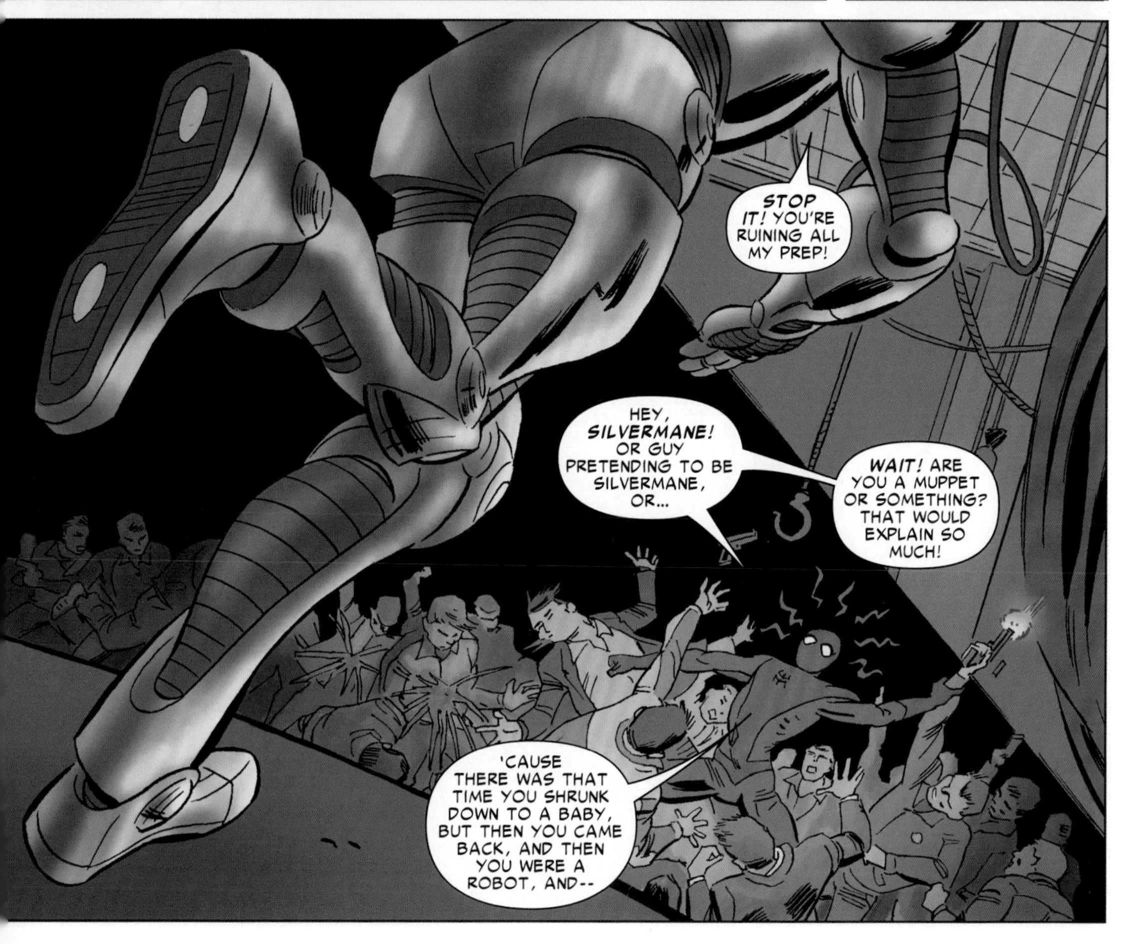
STOP IT! YOU'RE RUINING ALL MY PREP!
HEY, SILVERMANE! OR GUY PRETENDING TO BE SILVERMANE, OR...
WAIT! ARE YOU A MUPPET OR SOMETHING? THAT WOULD EXPLAIN SO MUCH!
'CAUSE THERE WAS THAT TIME YOU SHRUNK DOWN TO A BABY, BUT THEN YOU CAME BACK, AND THEN YOU WERE A ROBOT, AND--

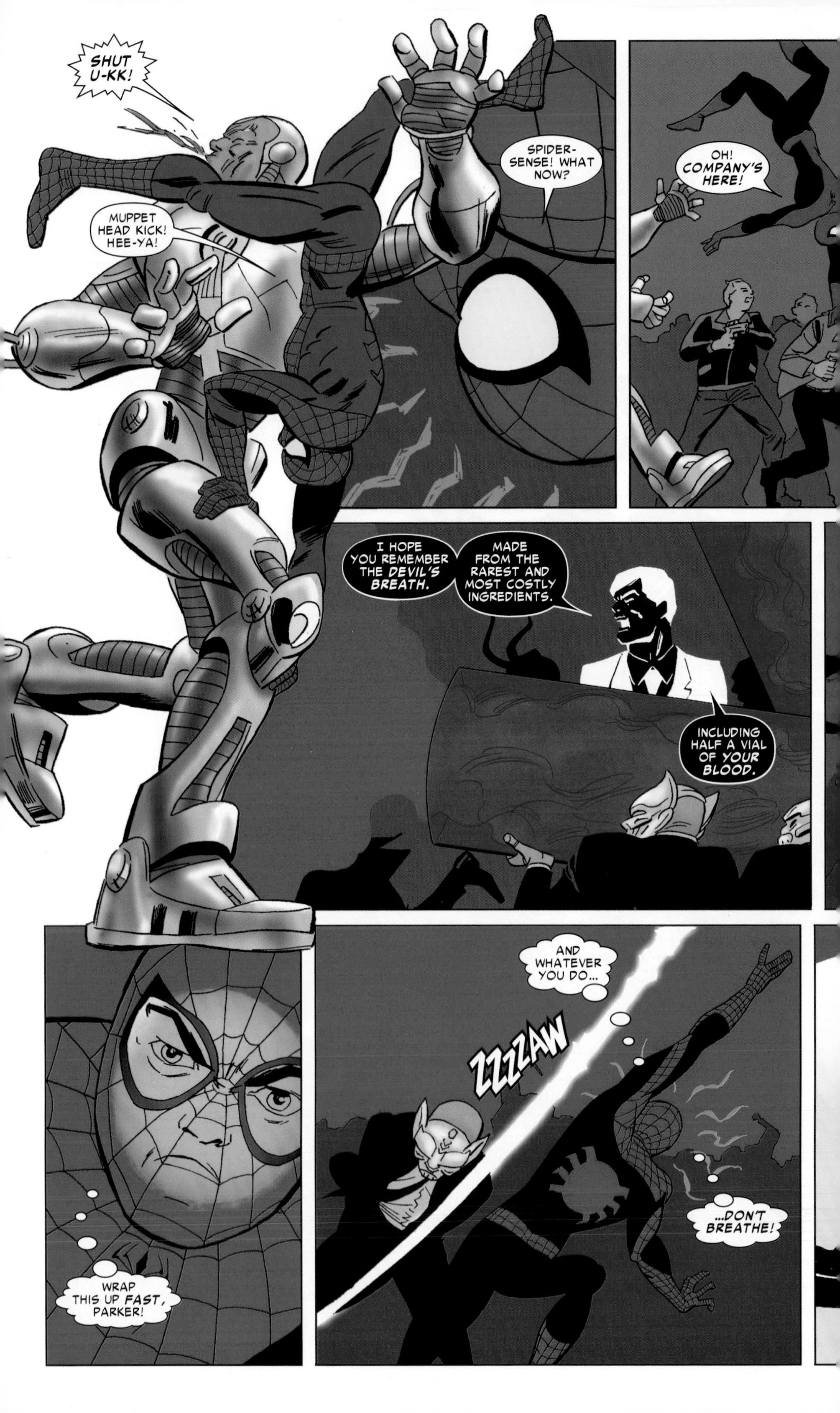
SHUT U-KK!
MUPPET HEAD KICK! HEE-YA!
SPIDER-SENSE! WHAT NOW?
OH! COMPANY'S HERE!
I HOPE YOU REMEMBER THE DEVIL'S BREATH.
MADE FROM THE RAREST AND MOST COSTLY INGREDIENTS.
INCLUDING HALF A VIAL OF YOUR BLOOD.
WRAP THIS UP FAST, PARKER!
AND WHATEVER YOU DO...
ZZZZAW
...DON'T BREATHE!

RRRAHHHHHHHH
. NEGATIVE? BEEN *AGES!* HAT'VE YOU EEN UP TO?
ACTUALLY, SPIDER-MAN, I'VE BEEN PREPARING A SPECIAL GIFT. JUST FOR YOU.

THAT'S NEGATIVE'S POISON GAS! THE STUFF THAT TARGETS *SPECIFIC DNA!*
OH, MAN! ONE WHIFF OF THAT AND IT'S GOODBYE, SPIDEY!

HAAA!

IT APPEARS I'VE ACCOMPLISHED THE IMPOSSIBLE.
I PUT AN END TO YOUR INCESSANT BABBLING! *HA HA!*

KEEP IT UP. IF I DON'T PASS OUT AND DIE, YOU ARE *SO* GONNA PAY FOR THAT!

ALL RIGHT, EVERYONE'S IN PLACE. IT'S SHOWTIME.
DANIEL, HAS ALL THE MAGGIA'S MONEY BEEN SWAPPED OUT FOR COUNTERFEIT BILLS?
YES, SIR.
GETAWAY VEHICLE'S READY?
FUELED AND DOCKED.
VERY GOOD.

OH, FRANCIS, IN CASE THE WALL-CRAWLER ESCAPES--THAT GAS WAS FREAKING HIM OUT.
SWITCH MY SMOKE BOMBS FROM GREEN TO RED, AND PREP GAG THIRTY-TWO.
NICE ONE, BOSS.

FIRE IN THE HOLE.
ALL I NEED NOW IS A VOLUNTEER FROM THE AUDIENCE.

SILVERMANE! I'VE WAITED A LONG TIME FOR THIS!
PERFECT.
SO YOU'RE NEGATIVE! THE FREAK FROM CHINATOWN WHO THINKS HE CAN MOVE IN ON MY TERRITORY!
I BEEN DYIN' TO GET MY HANDS ON YOU!

YOU DON'T REMEMBER ME, DO YOU? I DON'T CARE.
KLUNK
ALL THAT MATTERS IS THAT I'M THE LAST THING YOU'LL EVER SEE.

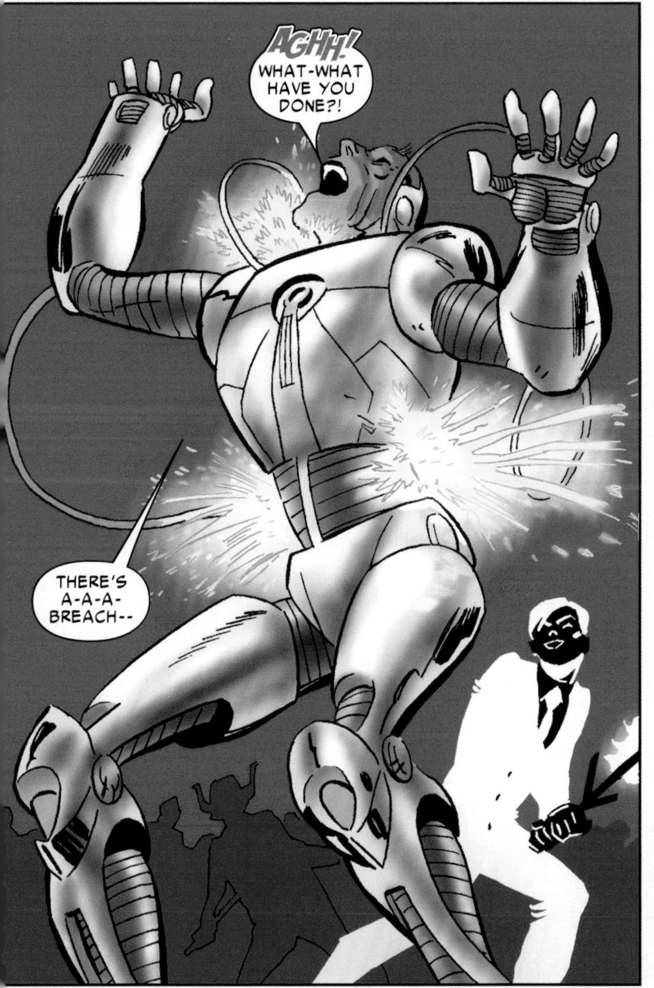
AGHH! WHAT-WHAT HAVE YOU DONE?!
THERE'S A-A-A-BREACH--

--IN MY P-P-POWER SUPPLY!
I LIVE FOR THIS! NOTHING BEATS A GOOD DEATH SCENE!
CAN'T CON-CON-CON--
GOD, I'M GOOD.
--CONTAIN IT!
Y'KNOW IT'S A SHAME...

...THAT SUPER VILLAINS DON'T GIVE OUT AWARDS FOR THIS STUFF.
NO!

SPIDER-SENSE JUST KICKED INTO HIGH GEAR! GOTTA GET EVERYONE OUT OF HERE-- FAST!
BUT I CAN'T EVEN YELL OUT! THERE'S NO WAY TO WARN 'EM! WHAT AM I GONNA DO?!!

COOPER? WHY ARE YOU HERE? WE DIDN'T CALL FOR FORENSICS.
CAPTAIN, WHAT'RE YOUR MEN DOING OUTSIDE? GUNSHOTS'VE BEEN REPORTED. IF THE GANG WAR'S IN THERE--
THEN IT'S IN A SECLUDED AREA. NO CIVILIANS AT RISK. I'M NOT PUTTING ANY OF MY MEN IN HARM'S WAY. WE WAIT FOR SPECIAL OPS.
BUT I KNOW SOME PEOPLE IN THERE! YOU HAVE TO--
NYPD

KRRRRASH

SPIDER-MAN?!
BUT HE'S ALONE! HE'S THE ONLY ONE WHO--

HUUHHH!

SPIDEY! THE MAN YOU WERE FOLLOWING IS HE--WAS HE--

HUH-HUH- HE WASN'T IN THERE. *HUH.* I DIDN'T SEE HIM.
NEGATIVE'S MEN. MAGGIA. A SILVERMANE MUPPET. GIMME A SEC TO CATCH MY BREATH...
WHO ARE WE TALKING ABOUT? WHO **WAS** IN THERE?
...THEN I'M GOIN' BACK IN. PLACE IS FLOODED WITH DEVIL'S BREATH. A POISON DESIGNED TO KILL ME--AND ONLY ME.

I REMEMBER IT, FROM THE VANDAMEER MASSACRE! I WAS ONE OF THE FIRST ON THE SCENE.[*]
HERE. ALL UNITS CARRY HAZMAT GEAR. THIS SHOULD HELP...
YPD
ASM #548--STEVE.

THIS'S A **LOT** OF SCRATCH, BOSS. WHAT'RE WE GONNA DO WITH IT ALL?
DON'T KNOW ABOUT YOU, BOYS. BUT I'M GONNA BUY AN ISLAND IN THE TROPICS...
...WHERE I'LL SIT UNDER PALM TREES AND DRINK THINGS OUTTA COCONUTS. THAT'S THE PLAN.

NOT HAPPENING, FISHBOWL! YOU JUST KILLED A LOT OF PEOPLE BACK THERE!
THERE'S ONLY TWO PLACES YOU'RE GOING STRAIGHT TO JAIL OR BACK IN THE GROUND!
C'MON, WEB-HEAD. ADMIT IT. YOU MISSED ME.
HOW'D YOU DO IT, BECK? HOW'RE YOU NOT DEAD?!
I DUNNO. MAYBE IT'S SOMETHING TO DO WITH BEING A MAST OF ILLUSION. DUH!
WHSSSH
THUD
ACTUALLY, I'VE BEEN AROUND FOR SOME TIME. YOU JUST DIDN'T KNOW IT.
ALL THESE LITTLE THINGS THAT'RE WRONG WITH YOUR LIFE...
THOK
...THE LIVING WHO SHOULD BE DEAD. THE DEAD WHO APPEAR TO BE LIVING.
IT'S ALL BEEN ME. MESSING WITH YOU. FOR ALL THE TIMES YOU MESSED WITH ME.
KRAK
NO! I'M NOT FALLING FOR ANY OF THIS!

HUHHH AKK HAKK KAFF
GIVE IT UP, MYSTERIO.
THE DEVIL'S BREATH ONLY TARGETS SOMEONE WITH MY DNA.
YES... SH-SHOULD HAVE TOLD YOU... KAFF...ALL THIS TIME...I WAS... REALLY...
...YOUR COUSIN!
WHAT THE--?!
GNYEAH!
PSYCH!
THUG
GROING
AH AH AHHH...
SUNNUVA BISCUIT!
I SWEAR WE SHOULD GIVE OUT AWARDS...

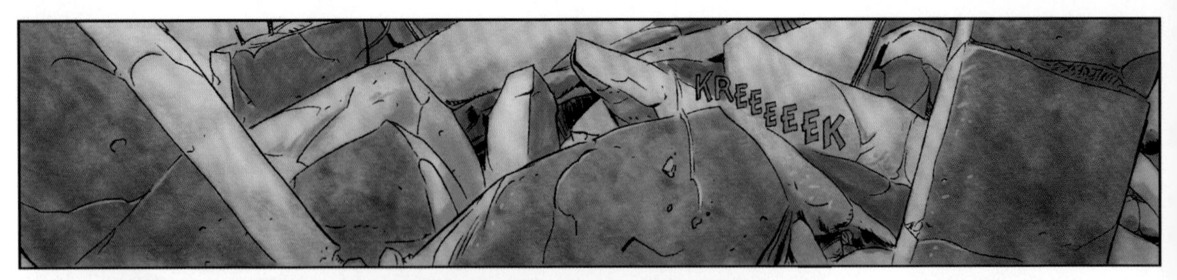
KREEEEEEK

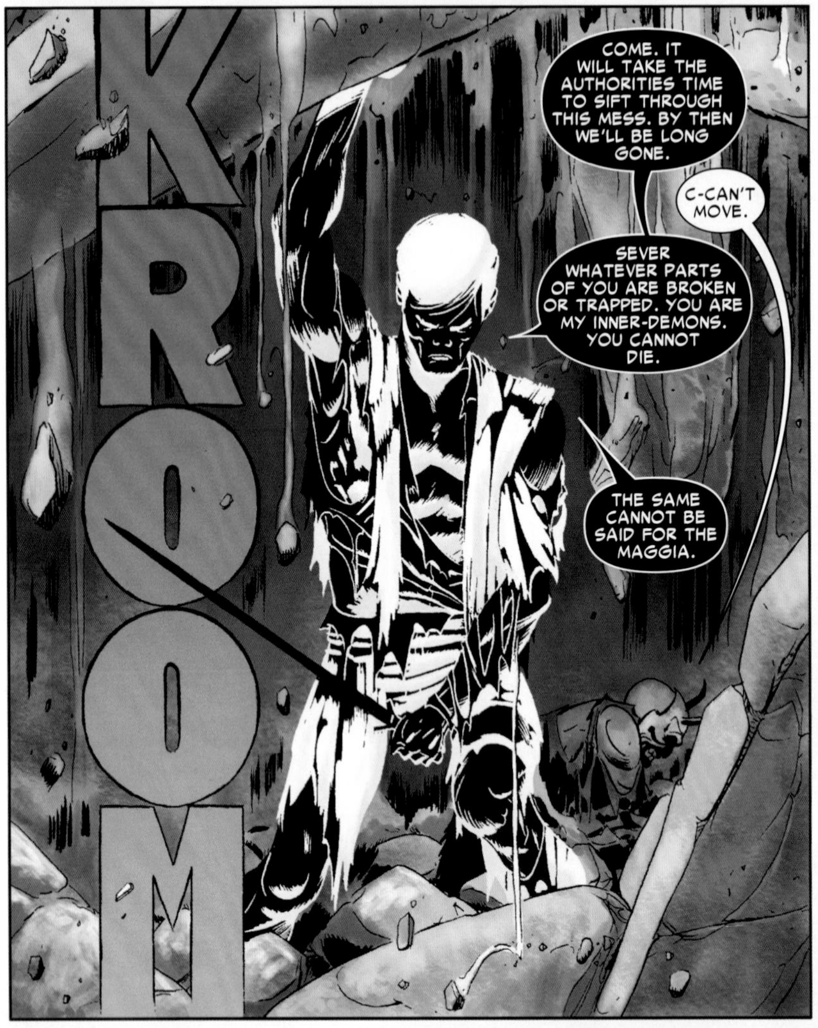
KROOM
COME. IT WILL TAKE THE AUTHORITIES TIME TO SIFT THROUGH THIS MESS. BY THEN WE'LL BE LONG GONE.
C-CAN'T MOVE.
SEVER WHATEVER PARTS OF YOU ARE BROKEN OR TRAPPED. YOU ARE MY INNER-DEMONS. YOU CANNOT DIE.
THE SAME CANNOT BE SAID FOR THE MAGGIA.

AND WHILE I WOULD HAVE LIKED TO ADD THEIR COFFERS TO MY OWN...IT DOESN'T MATTER.
THEY'RE GONE, SILVERMANE IS DEAD BY MY HAND, AND THE SPIDER HAS FINALLY LEARNED HIS PLACE. ALL IN ALL? THIS WAS A GOOD DAY.

EASY, CAPTAIN. WE GO IN WHEN THE CHIEF SAYS IT'S SECURE.
I DOUBT ANYONE'S GETTING OUT OF THERE. LET US DO OUR JOBS, CAPTAIN.
BUT THEY COULD BE--
F.D.N.Y
JUST 'CAUSE SPIDEY DIDN'T SEE HIM, DOESN'T MEAN HE WASN'T IN THERE. HOW DO I KNOW IF HE'S--
BZZZZZ
C-BEAR, READY 2 GO. WHERE R U?

YOU HEARD ME, PEOPLE. LOCK IT DOWN.
IF WE CAN'T GO IN, SURE AS HELL NOTHING'S GETTING OUT! C'MON, I'M RUNNIN' A TIGHT SHIP HERE!
WHOOOO

D THAT'S HOW YOU DO . THE OL' SLOW BOAT GETAWAY. Y'SMELL THAT, BOYS?
SMELLS LIKE A GARBAGE BARGE, BOSS.

NAH. THAT'S THE SWEET SMELL A' SUCCESS.
BUCHANAN
THWIP
MR. BECK'S VERY OWN CASH FOR TRASH PROGRAM.

NO KIDDIN'? HOW MUCH YOU THINK I'LL GET FOR A BIG OL' LIFE-SIZE PIECE OF GARBAGE...
...ONCE I FOLD IT IN HALF AND STUFF IT IN A LANDFILL?!
PIDER-MAN! ON T YOU EVER STOP?!

NOT NOW. YOU KILLED A LOT OF MEN TODAY, BECK. YOU'RE GOING DOWN.
THEY WERE MAGGIA! THEY WERE THE GARBAGE. WHAT? YOU GONNA GO AFTER YOUR PAL, THE PUNISHER NEXT?!
LOOK, YOU'RE SICK OF ME? FINE! I GOT MY ONE BIG SCORE! LET ME GO TO MY FREAKING ISLAND AND DRINK OUT OF A DAMN COCONUT! YOU'LL NEVER SEE ME AGAIN!
RIGHT. LIKE THIS WAS ABOUT THE MONEY? NO. IT WAS ABOUT THE THRILL. PLANNING THE PERFECT STUNT AND PULLING IT OFF.
THAT'S HOW YOU'RE WIRED. YOU'RE THE ONE WHO'LL NEVER STOP.

WHIRRK
HEH. YOU'RE RIGHT. BUT HERE'S THE THING, I KNOW HOW YOU'RE WIRED.
SURFACE-TO-AIR-MISSILE. WITH YOUR SPIDER-SENSE, I'D NEVER BE ABLE TO HIT YOU. BUT YOUR FRIENDS, THE COPS ON THE SHORE?
THIS'LL GO ALL MICHAEL BAY ON THEIR #@$!

THAT SHOULD KEEP YOU BUSY FOR A WHILE.
BECK, DON'T--

FWOOOOSH
FIRE!
THWIP THWIP

TUG
NO!
THERE'S THREE POINT FIVE BILLION DOLLARS HERE! WE HAVE TO--
ABANDON SHIP! WOMEN AN' SPIDERS FIRST!

I HATE YOU.

D'YOU THINK HE'S...?
PLEASE. HE'S MYSTERIO.
HE'S PROBABLY HALFWAY TO HOBOKEN BY NOW.

OOH, COFFEE! THANKS, CARLIE.
ANYTHING FOR YOU, SPIDEY. SPEAKING OF WHICH...
THAT TRACER YOU HAD ME PUT ON MY DAD... GETTING ANY SIGNALS?
SORRY. AND THAT'S NOT A GOOD SIGN. WHEN CROOKS FIND 'EM, THEY DITCH 'EM.
EVERYBODY ELSE SAVES 'EM AND PUTS 'EM UP ON EBAY.

BY THE WAY, MY OFFICE IS CLEARING YOU OF THOSE MAGGIA MURDERS.
WHEW! GOOD TO KNOW.
THEY CAN ALL ROT IN HELL.

GEEZ, CAP. WHAT GOT INTO YOU?
THESE. THEY FOUND THEM IN THE WRECKAGE.

THE NEXT "DIRTY COP" THEY PLANNED ON "RESURRECTING" WAS JEAN DEWOLFF.
ON SECOND THOUGHT, ROTTING IN HELL'S TOO GOOD FOR 'EM.

I LIKE YOU, SPIDEY. YOU EVER NEED HELP, A RESOURCE IN THE DEPARTMENT, YOU COME TO ME.
THINK I'LL TAKE YOU UP ON THAT. IT'S UPFRONT. HONEST.
THE LAST THING I WANT TO DO IS MESS WITH SOMEONE'S HEAD TO GET WHAT I WANT, IN THE END...

"...THAT NEVER PAYS."
HMM.

Paradise Island
ENJOY THE SILENCE
Fly Air Tropical
NEW LOW, LOW FARES
GOD, HOW I HATE HIM.
QUENTIN BECK, A.K.A. MYSTERIO, YOU ARE UNDER ARREST.

NICE TRY, BUT SHE'S DEAD.
I KNOW, I THOUGHT YOU'D LIKE THAT TOUCH. IT'S VERY YOU.

CHAMELEON? LONG TIME, NO SEE. SO WHAT'VE YOU BEEN UP TO?
MAKING SOME NEW FRIENDS...

AND THEY'RE DYING TO MEET YOU!

the AMAZING SPIDER-MAN
APPROVED BY THE COMICS CODE AUTHORITY
IND.
MARVEL COMICS GROUP 12¢
13 JUNE
WE'VE DONE IT! WE'VE CREATED THE GREATEST VILLAIN OF ALL FOR OL' SPIDEY!
"MYSTERIO!"
WHO, OR WHAT IS HE?

WHAT'S THIS?? SPIDER-MAN TURNING TO CRIME?? YOU'RE IN FOR A REAL SHOCK!

EVER SEE A COMIC MAG SUPER-HERO TAKE HIS TROUBLES TO A PSYCHIATRIST? YOU WILL NOW!

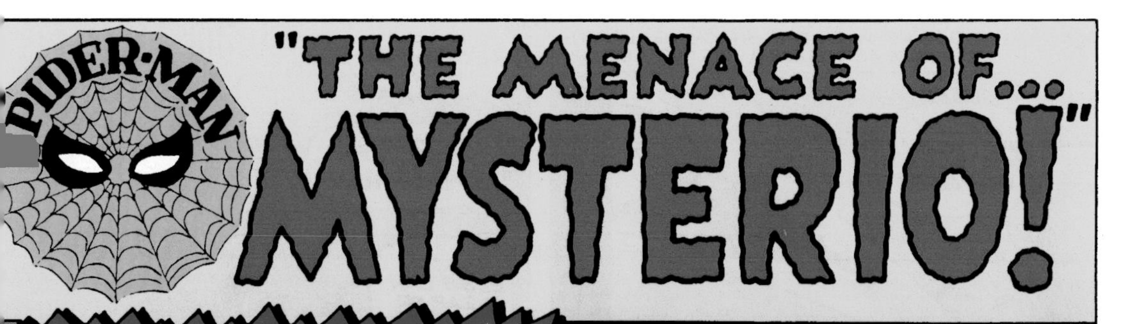
SPIDER-MAN
"THE MENACE OF... MYSTERIO!"

CAN WE BELIEVE OUR EYES? HAS THE AMAZING SPIDER-MAN TURNED TO CRIME?

THE EDITORS SINCERELY FEEL THAT THIS MAY WELL BE ONE OF THE MOST GRIPPING TALES OF THE YEAR!

PRESENTED WITH PRIDE BY ONE OF THE MOST FAMOUS TEAMS IN COMICS:
STAN LEE, *AUTHOR*
STEVE DITKO, *ARTIST*
LETTERED BY: ART SIMEK

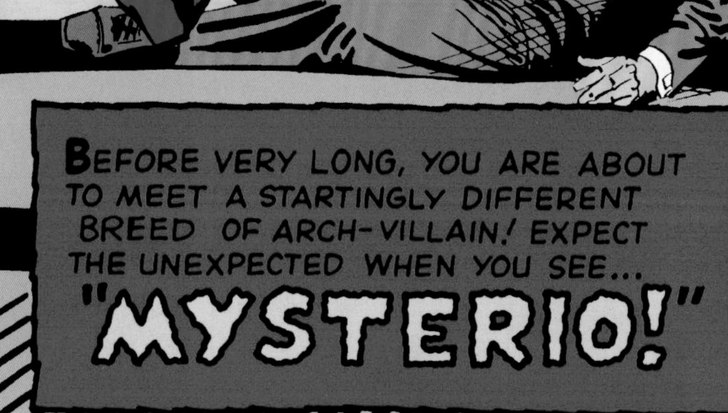
BEFORE VERY LONG, YOU ARE ABOUT TO MEET A STARTINGLY DIFFERENT BREED OF ARCH-VILLAIN! EXPECT THE UNEXPECTED WHEN YOU SEE...
"MYSTERIO!"

x-670 1

OUR TALE BEGINS WITH THE SHOCKING SUDDENNESS OF A SUMMER STORM, AS WE SEE...
HELP! POLICE! I'VE BEEN ROBBED!
THERE HE GOES! HE'S GETTING AWAY!

DID YOU RECOGNIZE HIM??
OF COURSE! IT WAS SPIDER-MAN!
NOBODY ELSE CAN LEAP OR CLIMB SHEER WALLS LIKE THAT!

WATCHMEN! ON THE ROOF! WELL, THIS WILL TAKE CARE OF THEM!
LOOK OUT--HE'S TANGLING US UP IN THAT WEB OF HIS!

HURRY--WE'VE GOT TO CUT OURSELVES FREE!
TOO LATE! HE'S GETTING AWAY!

SECONDS LATER, HIDDEN BY A SLOW, ROLLING FOG WHICH SPREADS OVER THE CITY, BLOTTING OUT THE MOONLIGHT, THE COLORFUL FIGURE DRIFTS SILENTLY TO THE GROUND, USING A HASTILY-IMPROVISED PARACHUTE MADE OF THIN, STRONG WEBBING!

THEN, AFTER THE WATCHMEN HAVE FREED THEMSELVES...
HE GOT AWAY, BUT AT LEAST WE KNOW WHO IT WAS! IT WAS SPIDER-MAN!
WE'LL GET HIM SOONER OR LATER BUT I NEVER THOUGHT HE'D REAL TURN TO CRIME!

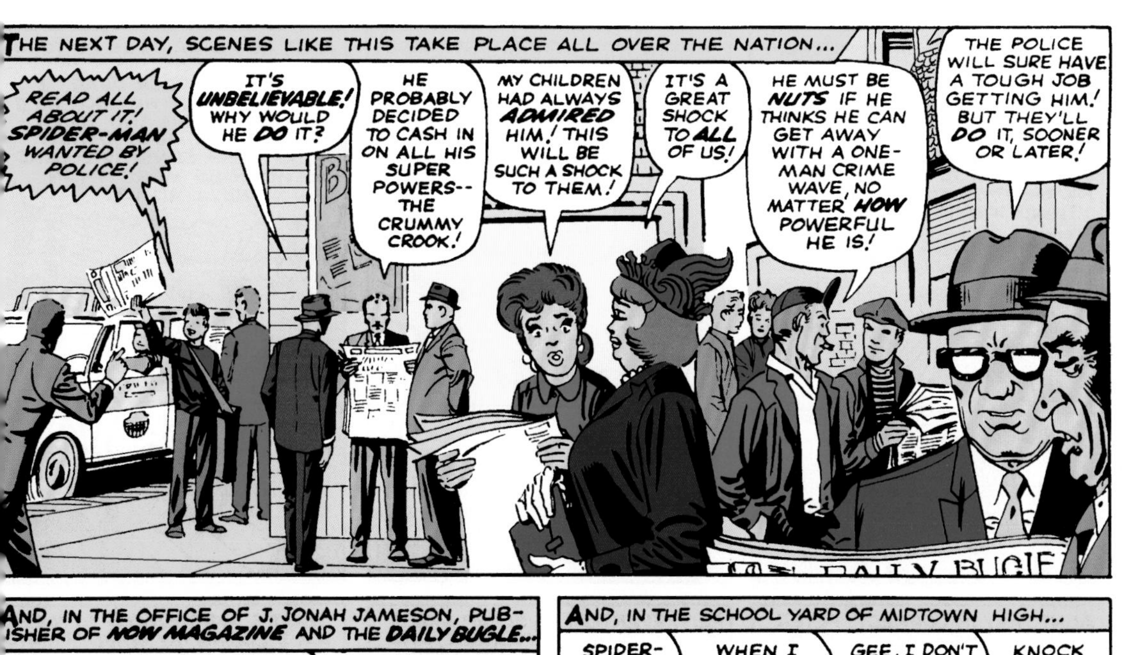
THE NEXT DAY, SCENES LIKE THIS TAKE PLACE ALL OVER THE NATION...
READ ALL ABOUT IT! SPIDER-MAN WANTED BY POLICE!
IT'S UNBELIEVABLE! WHY WOULD HE DO IT?
HE PROBABLY DECIDED TO CASH IN ON ALL HIS SUPER POWERS-- THE CRUMMY CROOK!
MY CHILDREN HAD ALWAYS ADMIRED HIM! THIS WILL BE SUCH A SHOCK TO THEM!
IT'S A GREAT SHOCK TO ALL OF US!
HE MUST BE NUTS IF HE THINKS HE CAN GET AWAY WITH A ONE-MAN CRIME WAVE, NO MATTER HOW POWERFUL HE IS!
THE POLICE WILL SURE HAVE A TOUGH JOB GETTING HIM! BUT THEY'LL DO IT, SOONER OR LATER!
DAILY BUGLE

AND, IN THE OFFICE OF J. JONAH JAMESON, PUBLISHER OF NOW MAGAZINE AND THE DAILY BUGLE...
FIND ALL THE OLD EDITORIALS I WROTE, ACCUSING SPIDER-MAN OF BEING A MENACE! I WANT TO REPRINT THEM NOW, SO PEOPLE CAN SEE HOW RIGHT I WAS!
I CAN'T BELIEVE THIS OF SPIDER-MAN! I STILL REMEMBER HOW HE ONCE SAVED MY LIFE...!*
*SPIDER-MAN #11 - EDITOR.

AND, IN THE SCHOOL YARD OF MIDTOWN HIGH...
SPIDER-MAN SURE HAD ALL OF US FOOLED!
WHEN I THINK HOW WE MADE A HERO OF HIM--WHAT FOOLS WE WERE!
GEE, I DON'T KNOW, LIZ! WE CAN'T BE POSITIVE! HE MAY STILL BE INNOCENT!
KNOCK IT OFF, FLASH! HE'S GUILTY AND YOU KNOW IT!

AND NOW, THE MOMENT WE'VE BEEN WAITING FOR! LET'S VISIT SPIDER-MAN HIMSELF-- IN HIS EVERYDAY IDENTITY AS PETER PARKER, TEEN-AGE STUDENT...
THIS IS IMPOSSIBLE! IT'S INSANE! I KNOW I DIDN'T COMMIT THAT CRIME! AND YET-- THOSE WITNESSES! THAT EVIDENCE!

IT COULDN'T HAVE BEEN AN IMPOSTER! NOBODY ELSE CAN SHOOT A WEB AS I DO-- OR CLIMB SHEER WALLS THE WAY I CAN WITH MY SPIDER POWER!!

THERE'S ONLY ONE OTHER ANSWER-- BUT IT'S TOO AWFUL TO THINK ABOUT--
AM I BECOMING A SPLIT-PERSONALITY?? LIKE DR. JEKYLL AND MR. HYDE?? PERHAPS-- PERHAPS I DID IT IN MY SLEEP-- WITHOUT KNOWING?!!

MINUTES LATER, IN THE KITCHEN...
GOSH! SORRY, AUNT MAY--THAT'S THE SECOND DISH I'VE DROPPED TODAY!
PETER DEAR, YOU DON'T SEEM TO BE YOURSELF! IS ANYTHING WRONG?

YOU'RE NOT WORRIED BECAUSE OUR SAVINGS ACCOUNT IS ALMOST GONE, AND IT'S GETTING HARDER TO PAY THE MORTGAGE EACH MONTH, ARE YOU? WE'LL MAKE OUT SOMEHOW, DEAR!
I KNOW, AUNT MAY! MAYBE I'VE BEEN STUDYING TOO HARD! I'LL JUST TRY TO GET SOME SLEEP!

AND, AS PETER GOES UP TO HIS ROOM...
THE POOR DEAR! I WORRY ABOUT HIM SO! HE'S NOT AS ROUGH AND THICK-SKINNED AS MOST OTHER BOYS! HE'S SENSITIVE--AND HE WORRIES MORE THAN HE'LL ADMIT!

AUNT MAY IS CORRECT! PETER PARKER IS WORRIED--ABOUT SOMETHING SHE'D NEVER SUSPECT!
I NEVER THOUGHT THIS WOULD HAPPEN TO ME! I-I'M AFRAID TO SHUT MY EYES--TO GO TO SLEEP!

BUT, EVENTUALLY, SLEEP DOES COME TO PETER PARKER, AND --THE NEXT MORNING, WHEN HE AWAKES...
BULLETIN! SPIDER-MAN HAS STRUCK AGAIN DURING THE NIGHT!
OH NO!!

WHAT'S HAPPENING TO ME?? AM I LOSING MY MIND?? MAYBE I'M GOING MAD--DOING THINGS I CAN'T REMEMBER THE NEXT MORNING?!!
THERE'S ONLY ONE THING TO DO--ONLY ONE WAY TO FIND OUT--

AND SO, A SHORT TIME LATER, IN THE OFFICE OF A NEARBY PSYCHIATRIST...
DON'T BE ALARMED, DOC! I JUST WANT TO KNOW ONE THING! CAN A PERSON DO SOMETHING IN HIS SLEEP THAT HE'D NEVER DO AWAKE?
SPIDER-MAN! IF I CAN MAKE A PATIENT OUT OF HIM, I'LL MAKE MEDICAL HISTORY! IMAGINE, A MYSTERIOUS SUPER-HERO WHO'S A MENTAL CASE!

I THINK I CAN HELP YOU! JUST COME DOWN FROM THAT WALL AND LIE DOWN ON THE COUCH! I'LL TRY TO PROBE INTO YOUR SUBCONSCIOUS! DON'T BE NERVOUS!
OKAY, DOC--BUT NO TRICKS, HEAR?

UST MAKE YOURSELF OMFORTABLE HERE! RELAX-- AND THEN TELL ME ANYTHING THAT COMES INTO YOUR HEAD!
I APPRECIATE THIS, DOCTOR! IF YOU CAN HELP ME, I--
OH NO! WHAT A MISTAKE I ALMOST MADE! IF I JUST RELAX AND SAY WHATEVER I THINK OF, I'M LIABLE TO GIVE AWAY MY SECRET IDENTITY! I DON'T DARE!

SORRY, DOC-- I JUST CHANGED MY MIND! IT LOOKS LIKE I'LL HAVE TO FIND ANOTHER SOLUTION! SORRY TO HAVE BOTHERED YOU!
WAIT! COME BACK! YOU'RE THE KIND OF PATIENT EVERY PSYCHIATRIST DREAMS OF! STOP!

A SHORT TIME LATER, AT THE OFFICES OF THE DAILY BUGLE...
PETER, WHAT'S WRONG! YOU LOOK SO DEJECTED...!
NOTHING, BETTY! I'M OKAY!

YOU'RE PROBABLY WORRIED BECAUSE YOU HAVEN'T SOLD ANY NEWS PHOTOS TO MR. JAMESON LATELY! OH, PETER, IF ONLY YOU'D FIND SOME DIFFERENT TYPE OF WORK!
LAY OFF, WILLYA, BETTY? I'M IN NO MOOD TO BE PREACHED TO!

YOU'RE ALWAYS SAYING THAT IT'S TOO DANGEROUS TO TRY TO TAKE EX-CLUSIVE CRIME PHOTOS! I DON'T TELL YOU HOW TO LIVE YOUR LIFE-- DON'T BUTT INTO MINE!
Y-YOU NEVER SPOKE TO ME THAT WAY BEFORE!!

THEN, PETER ENTERS THE PRIVATE OFFICE OF A JUBILANT J. JONAH JAMESON...
LOOK AT THESE LETTERS -THESE TELEGRAMS! THE PUBLIC FINALLY SAYS I WAS RIGHT ABOUT SPIDER-MAN! WHAT A GREAT TRIUMPH THIS IS FOR ME!
I'M GLAD YOU'RE IN A GOOD MOOD, MISTER JAMESON! I, EH, NEED A LOAN! MY AUNT HAS A MORTGAGE PAYMENT TO MAKE, AND WE'RE A LITTLE SHORT...

WHY TELL ME? I'M NOT A BANK! YOU KNOW MY RULE, PARKER-- I DON'T LEND MONEY! I'M BUSY NOW! YOU KNOW WHERE THE DOOR IS!
BUT I'M NOT ASKING FOR MUCH-- JUST A LITTLE TILL I GET SOME PICTURES FOR YOU!
5

DON'T TRY TO TAKE ADVANTAGE OF ME BECAUSE I'M SO SOFT-HEARTED! THE ANSWER IS NO! UNLESS--YOU WANT TO SELL ME THE SECRET OF HOW YOU TAKE THOSE GREAT CRIME PHOTOS OF YOURS?
NO DICE!

I KNOW YOU MUST HAVE SOME SORT OF SPECIAL CAMERA--!!
IMAGINE IF I EVER TOLD HIM I WEAR IT IN MY BELT--WHEN I'M DRESSED AS SPIDER-MAN, SWINGING OVER THE CITY ON MY WEB!
THANKS FOR NOTHING, MR. JAMESON!

FINALLY...
I KNOW I SHOULDN'T DO THIS WHILE THE WHOLE CITY IS HUNTING FOR SPIDER-MAN!
BUT THE ONLY WAY I CAN GET THE MORTGAGE MONEY FOR AUNT MAY IS TO TAKE SOME NEWS PIX WHICH JJJ WILL PAY ME FOR!

IF I'M LUCKY, I MAY SPOT A CRIME BEING COMMITTED WHILE I SWING THRU TOWN...
LOOK! IT'S SPIDER-MAN!

AFTER HIM!
CALL THE POLICE!
DON'T LET HIM GET AWAY!

IT'S WORSE THAN I THOUGHT! THE PUBLIC HATES ME NOW!

AND THE TERRIBLE THING ABOUT IT IS--I DON'T KNOW IF THEY'RE RIGHT!
I CAN'T MAKE THE MONEY I NEED--AND I MAY BE COMMITTING CRIMES WITHOUT KNOWING IT! BOY! LIFE SURE IS A BOWL OF CHERRIES!

THE NEXT DAY, ON THE WAY TO HIGH SCHOOL...
I DON'T KNOW WHAT TO WORRY ABOUT FIRST! PAYING THE MORTGAGE, OR WONDERING IF I'M A SLEEP-WALKING CRIMINAL?!!
PETER! WAIT FOR ME!

I'VE BEEN WANTING TO SHOW YOU MY NEW HAIRDO! DO YOU LIKE IT?
SURE, LIZ! IT'S REAL NICE!
OF ALL TIMES TO HAVE TO TALK ABOUT A GAL'S HAIR!

WHAT NUTTY TIMING! FOR MONTHS LIZ WOULDN'T GIVE ME A TUMBLE, BUT SINCE I'VE BEEN DATING BETTY, LIZ HAS GOTTEN A CRUSH ON ME!
YOU LOOK UPSET, PETER! IS ANYTHING WRONG?

WOW! IS THAT QUESTION THE UNDERSTATEMENT OF THE YEAR!!
NAW, EVERYTHING'S GREAT, LIZ! IF IT GETS ANY BETTER I'LL SHOOT MYSELF!
OH, PETER! I ALWAYS KNEW YOU HAD A GREAT SENSE OF HUMOR!

MEANWHILE, A FEW YARDS AWAY...
QUIT KIDDIN', FLASH! YOU DON'T REALLY THINK SPIDER-MAN IS INNOCENT, DO YOU?
YOU'RE DARN RIGHT I DO! LET ME TELL YOU--
HEY! LOOK AT THAT!! WOW-WEEE!

GOSH, LIZ, I ALMOST DIDN'T RECOGNIZE YOU! YOU'RE BEAUTIFUL NOW!
REALLY, MISTER THOMPSON?? AND WHAT WAS I BEFORE, PRAY TELL??
POOR FLASH! HE ALWAYS SAYS THE WRONG THING!!

MEANWHILE, AT J. JONAH JAMESON'S OFFICE...
WHAT DID YOU CALL THIS MEETING FOR, J.J.?
SOME NUT SENT ME A NOTE SAYING HE COULD GET RID OF SPIDER-MAN SINGLE-HANDED! I TOLD HIM TO COME UP HERE AND PROVE IT!
LOOK AT THE DOOR...!

I AM MYSTERIO!
WHAT A GET-UP! HE'S CORNIER-LOOKING THAN SPIDER-MAN!
7

THERE IS A **REASON** FOR MY DISGUISE! IF THE UNDERWORLD EVER FINDS OUT ABOUT MY "**POWERS**", THEY MIGHT TRY TO STOP ME BY THREATENING MY FAMILY!

POWERS? WHAT POWERS?
HOW DO WE KNOW IT'S NOT A **TRICK?** YOU COULD BE SPIDER-MAN **HIMSELF** UNDER THAT FISHBOWL!
YOU WILL LEAR SOON ENOUGH THAT I **MEAN** WHAT I SAY! **MYSTERIO** DOE NOT LIE!

I MUST GO NOW! IF YOU WISH TO END THE MENACE OF SPIDER-MAN, FOLLOW THE INSTRUCTIONS IN THIS ENVELOPE!

REMEMBER, ALTHOUGH SPIDER-MAN HAS GREAT POWERS, THE POWER OF **MYSTERIO** IS EVEN GREATER!
WHERE'D THAT **SMOKE** COME FROM?? H-HE'S **DIS-APPEARING!**

HE'S **GONE!** WH-WHAT KIND OF A PERSON **WAS** HE??
QUIET! I'LL SEE WHAT THIS LETTER SAYS...

I DON'T **GET** IT! BUT IT MUST MAKE SENSE, OR MYSTERIO WOULDN'T HAVE GONE TO ALL THIS TROUBLE!
PRINT A NOTICE IN THE DAILY BUGLE SAYING: IF SPIDER-MAN WANTS TO LEARN THE **TRUTH** ABOUT HIMSELF, HE SHOULD MEET MYSTERIO ATOP THE BROOKLYN BRIDGE!

DID YOU SEE **THAT??** THE LETTER **VANISHED**-- IN A PUFF OF SMOKE!
Y'KNOW, JJ, IF SPIDER-MAN **CAN** BE BEATEN, I'VE GOT A HUNCH THAT MYSTERIO IS THE ONE TO **DO** IT!

WELL, WE'VE GOT NOTHING TO LOSE! I'LL **PRINT** THAT NOTICE! AND IF IT MEANS THE END OF SPIDER-MAN, I'LL BECOME A **HERO** TO THE PEOPLE OF THIS CITY!
THAT'S RIGHT, J J!

THE NEXT DAY...
DID YOU SEE THAT NOTICE IN THE BUGLE TODAY? I WONDER WHO MYSTERIO IS?
I DON'T KNOW, BUT ANYONE WITH SUCH A CORNY NAME MUST BE A PHONY!
THIS MAY BE THE CHANCE I'VE BEEN WAITING FOR! MAYBE MYSTERIO KNOWS WHAT'S BEHIND THE "SPIDER-MAN CRIME WAVE"! I'VE GOT TO MEET HIM!

WITHIN MINUTES, ONE OF THE WORLD'S MOST FAMOUS, MOST CONTROVERSIAL COSTUMED FIGURES APPROACHES THE BROOKLYN BRIDGE IN HIS OWN AMAZING MANNER...
I HOPE THE WHOLE THING ISN'T JUST A GAG-- BUT I CAN'T AFFORD NOT TO CHECK IT OUT!

I'VE GOT TO MOVE CAUTIOUSLY, IN CASE IT'S A TRAP! BUT HOW CAN IT BE?? THERE'S NO ONE IN SIGHT!

AND THEN, SUDDENLY-- UNEXPECTEDLY-- A FIGURE APPEARS!!
I AM MYSTERIO! I AM THE ONE WHO WILL, SINGLE-HANDEDLY, DESTROY SPIDER-MAN!
IT WASN'T A GAG! BUT IF THAT COSTUMED CLOWN THINKS I'M A SITTING DUCK, HE'S GOT ANOTHER THINK COMIN'!

I DON'T KNOW WHAT YOUR GAME IS, MYSTERIO, BUT--HEY!
OVER-CONFIDENT FOOL! MY POWER IS GREATER THAN YOURS!

SEE HOW EASILY I CAN AVOID YOUR ATTACK WHILE SPRINGING BEHIND YOU AND LAUNCHING ONE OF MY OWN!
OHHH...

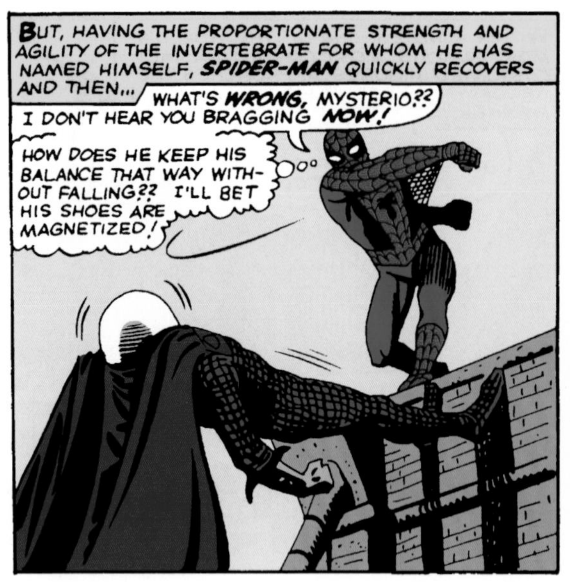
BUT, HAVING THE PROPORTIONATE STRENGTH AND AGILITY OF THE INVERTEBRATE FOR WHOM HE HAS NAMED HIMSELF, SPIDER-MAN QUICKLY RECOVERS AND THEN...
WHAT'S WRONG, MYSTERIO?? I DON'T HEAR YOU BRAGGING NOW!
HOW DOES HE KEEP HIS BALANCE THAT WAY WITH-OUT FALLING?? I'LL BET HIS SHOES ARE MAGNETIZED!

WELL, I'LL JUST GRAB HIM AND-- HOLY COW! HE DODGED ME AGAIN!
DID YOU THINK YOU COULD BEAT MYSTERIO WITH ONE MEASLY BLOW?!!

THAT'S WHAT I GET FOR PULLING MY PUNCH BECAUSE I WANT TO TAKE HIM ALIVE!
WELL, IF A WALLOP CAN'T BEAT YOU, LET'S SEE WHAT A WEB CAN DO!

I TOLD YOU MY POWER WAS GREATER! NOW WATCH ME PROVE IT!

I DON'T GET IT!! AT ONE GESTURE HE SEEMS TO BE STOPPING MY WEB IN MID-AIR!

THE WEB IS DISSOLVING-- VAPORIZING!! AS THOUGH IT'S BEEN SPRAYED WITH A FINE CHEMICAL MIST, TOO SMALL FOR THE EYE TO SEE!

TOO BAD, SPIDER-MAN! YOUR PUNY LITTLE BAG OF TRICKS IS ALMOST EXHAUSTED! BUT THERE IS NO LIMIT TO MY POWERS! SEE HOW EASILY I CAN ELUDE YOU ANY TIME I DESIRE!

THAT'S HIS FIRST BIG MISTAKE! HE CAN'T LOSE HIMSELF IN A CLOUD OF SMOKE! MY SPIDER SENSE WILL LEAD ME RIGHT TO HIM!

BUT, ONCE INSIDE THE THICK BILLOWY MIST...
THIS NEVER HAPPENED TO ME BEFORE! MY SPIDER SENSE ISN'T WORKING! IT'S AS THOUGH SOME-THING IS INTERFERING WITH IT-- JAMMING IT!!

CAN'T SEE HIM--NOR CAN I SENSE HIM! BUT I MUSTN'T GIVE UP! I'LL SWING WILDLY --MAYBE I'LL BE LUCKY!

BUT SPIDER-MAN'S LUCK SEEMS TO BE RUNNING TRUE TO ITS USUAL FORM--ALL BAD!
UGH! WHAT A SITUATION THIS IS! I CAN'T SEE HIM-- BUT HE SURE CAN SEE ME!

HE'S GOT TO BE NEAR ME SOMEWHERE! I'LL KEEP SWINGING!
HE PLANNED EVERY DETAIL OF THIS FIGHT-- EVEN FINDING A WAY TO JAM MY SPIDER SENSE!!

OHH! I'VE GOT TO DO SOME-THING! HE'S MAKING A HELP-LESS PUNCHING BAG OUT OF ME!!

MY SPIDER STRENGTH ENABLES ME TO RESIST BLOWS THAT WOULD KNOCK OUT NORMAL MEN-- BUT I'M STILL NOT INVULNERABLE!!

BESIDES, IT LOOKS AS THOUGH MYSTERIO DOES HAVE SUPER POWERS WHICH ARE AS GREAT AS MY OWN!! UGH!!
11

THE LONGER I STAY THERE, THE MORE PUNISHMENT I'LL TAKE!
ONLY ONE THING TO DO-- AND THIS IS IT!

THEN, AS SPIDER-MAN HITS THE WATER BELOW, THE DRAMATIC FIGURE OF MYSTERIO APPEARS ONCE AGAIN THRU THE BILLOWING MIST...
I'VE WON! IF SPIDER-MAN COULDN'T DEFEAT ME, THEN NOBODY CAN! NOW MYSTERIO IS SUPREME!

SECONDS LATER, POLICE HELICOPTERS APPEAR ON THE SCENE...
SPIDER-MAN HAS BEEN DEFEATED BY MYSTERIO! WE ARE PROCEEDING WITH "OPERATION PICK-UP"...

-WHEW!- WHAT A DROP! UH OH! POLICE WHIRLY-BIRDS! IF I DON'T MOVE FAST I'LL BE CAUGHT!

SPIDER-MAN SWIFTLY FASHIONS AN AIR-TIGHT WEB HELMET, AND PLACES IT OVER HIS HEAD...
THIS'LL ENABLE ME TO HOLD MY BREATH UNDER-WATER LONG ENOUGH TO GET TO SAFETY!

MINUTES LATER, AT A LONELY PIER...
WELL, ONE THING IS CERTAIN--A DEFEAT LIKE THIS WILL SURE KEEP ME FROM EVER GETTING TOO CONCEITED!

THEN, AFTER SILENTLY REACHING HIS HOME...
BUT THE DAY WASN'T A TOTAL LOSS! I DID LEARN THE ANSWER TO ONE OF THE THINGS THAT'S BEEN WORRYING ME!

HE NEXT DAY, CROWDS LINE FIFTH AVENUE AS A
OTORCADE DRIVES BY, LED BY A HAPPILY WAVING
OSTUMED FIGURE...
MYSTERIO DESERVES THIS PARADE! AT AST WE HAVE SOME- ONE WHO CAN BEAT SPIDER-MAN!
HOORAY FOR MYSTERIO! SPIDER-MAN WON'T DARE PULL ANY MORE CRIMES IN THIS CITY NOW!

AND AMONG THE TEEN-AGERS WATCHING THE THE PARADE, WE FIND...
STILL THINK SPIDER-MAN'S SO GREAT, FLASH?
DARN RIGHT I DO! MYSTERIO'S JUST A BIG PUBLICITY HOUND, IF YOU ASK ME! MY DOUGH IS STILL ON SPIDER-MAN!
Y'KNOW SOME-THING, FLASH? YOU'RE NOT AS DUMB AS YOU LOOK! IN FACT, YOU'RE OKAY, FELLA!

LOOK, PUNY PARKER, I DON'T NEED COMPLIMENTS FROM YOU! AND WHILE WE'RE TALKIN', I WANNA WARN YOU TO STAY AWAY FROM LIZ ALLAN! SHE'S MY GIRL FRIEND!
REALLY? TOO BAD. SHE DOESN'T SEEM TO THINK SO! BUT DON'T WORRY, BRIGHT EYES, YOU CAN HAVE HER!

A SHORT TIME LATER, AT THE OFFICE OF J. JONAH JAMESON...
I WANT THE MEMBERS OF MY STAFF TO MEET MYSTERIO, THE MAN WHO BEAT SPIDER-MAN!
MYSTERIO IS A REAL CRIME-FIGHTER! HE'S NOT AFRAID TO MEET PEOPLE AND TO BE INTER-VIEWED AS THAT COWARDLY SPIDER-MAN WAS!

AND ONCE MYSTERIO HAS DEFEATED SPIDER-MAN FOR GOOD, HE WILL REVEAL HIS TRUE IDENTITY EXCLUSIVELY TO MY NEWSPAPER! IT'LL BE THE SCOOP OF THE CENTURY FOR ME! RIGHT, MYSTERIO?
RIGHT! JUST SO LONG AS YOU REMEMBER THE MONEY YOU PROMISED ME!

MYSTERIO, I WANT YOU TO MEET PETER PARKER! DON'T LET HIS AGE FOOL YOU! DESPITE HIS YOUTH, HE'S THE BEST PHOTOGRAPHER I'VE GOT! I'LL EXPECT HIM TO TAKE SOME GREAT PICTURES OF YOUR NEXT FIGHT WITH SPIDER-MAN!
I'LL TRY NOT TO DISAPPOINT YOU-- BOTH OF YOU!
13

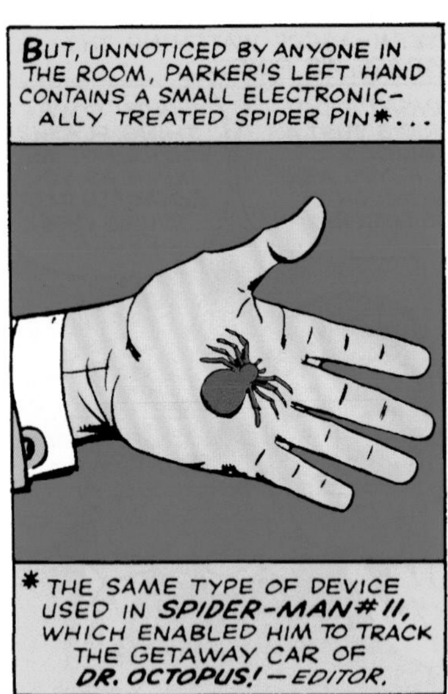
BUT, UNNOTICED BY ANYONE IN THE ROOM, PARKER'S LEFT HAND CONTAINS A SMALL ELECTRONICALLY TREATED SPIDER PIN*...
* THE SAME TYPE OF DEVICE USED IN SPIDER-MAN #11, WHICH ENABLED HIM TO TRACK THE GETAWAY CAR OF DR. OCTOPUS! — EDITOR.

WHILE NO ONE IS PAYING ATTENTION, I'LL JUST SLIP MY LITTLE SPIDER DEVICE IN THE FOLDS OF MYSTERIO'S CLOAK... LIKE THIS!

NOW I'LL BE ABLE TO TRACE HIS MOVEMENTS! THERE'S MORE TO MYSTERIO THAN MEETS THE EYES-- AND I'M GONNA FIND OUT WHAT IT IS!

THEN, AS PETER LEAVES JAMESON'S OFFICE...
I'M GLAD TO SEE YOU SMILING AGAIN, PETER! ARE YOU CELEBRATING SPIDER-MAN'S DEFEAT, ALSO?
NOT EXACTLY, BETTY!

IN FACT, I'M NOT SO SURE THAT SPIDER-MAN HAS BEEN DEFEATED! WELL, I HAVE TO RUSH NOW! SEE YOU LATER...
YOU'RE NOT SURE--?? BUT...

HMM! HE'S NEVER BEEN SO ANXIOUS TO LEAVE ME BEFORE! CAN HE HAVE MET ANOTHER GIRL? I'VE NOTICED A PRETTY BLONDE WITH HIM OCCASIONALLY...
OH, STOP IT, BETTY BRANT! YOU'RE BECOMING JEALOUS!

WHILE BEHIND THE DOOR TO JAMESON'S OFFICE...
I SHALL LEAVE YOU NOW, JAMESON! IN MY OWN MANNER! FAREWELL-- TILL NEXT TIME!

HE'S GONE! FOR HEAVEN'S SAKE, JJJ, HOW DOES HE DO IT?
WHO CARES? THE IMPORTANT THING IS THAT I'VE FINALLY FOUND SOMEONE WHO CAN BEAT SPIDER-MAN! I FEEL LIKE CELEBRATING!

BUT JAMESON MIGHT NOT FEEL SO TRIUMPHANT IF HE COULD SEE A DRAMATIC FIGURE ON A NEARBY ROOFTOP, WAITING TO RECEIVE THE ELECTRONIC SIGNAL FROM HIS HIDDEN SPIDER PIN!
AH, MY SPYING DEVICE IS BEGINNING TO REGISTER NOW!

WITHIN MINUTES, A PIERCING SPIDER SIGNAL FLASHES IN THE NIGHT OUTSIDE OF A TV MOVIE STUDIO BUILDING...
HOLD IT, MYSTERIO! WE'VE SOME UNFINISHED BUSINESS TO TAKE CARE OF!
SPIDER-MAN! HOW--??

YOU DIDN'T THINK I'D LET YOU CHOOSE THE TIME AND PLACE FOR OUR NEXT FIGHT, DID YOU?
BAH! IT DOESN'T MATTER WHERE WE BATTLE! I CAN BEAT YOU HERE AS I DID ON THE BRIDGE BEFORE!

ALL I NEED DO IS CREATE MY CONCEALING MIST, WHICH MAKES YOU UN-ABLE TO SEE ME!

AND WHICH ALSO DULLS YOUR SPIDER SENSE SO YOU CAN-NOT BE PREPARED FOR MY BLOWS!

DO I MAKE MYSELF CLEAR, SPIDER-MAN??

OR DO YOU WANT STILL MORE PROOF?? I CAN DO THIS ALL DAY!

OKAY, I GET THE MESSAGE! I CAN'T COPE WITH YOUR BAG OF TRICKS! BUT ADMIT ONE THING -- IT WAS YOU WHO COMMITTED THOSE CRIMES, DIS-GUISED AS ME, WASN'T IT?
OF COURSE! ONLY I HAVE THE GENIUS TO IMITATE -- IN FACT, TO IMPROVE UPON, YOUR OWN POWERS!

"I MIGHT AS WELL TELL YOU THE WHOLE STORY--FOR I SHALL SEE TO IT THAT YOU NEVER TELL ANYONE ELSE! I USED TO BE A MOVIE STUNT MAN--AND THEN I BECAME A SPECIAL EFFECTS MAN FOR TV MOVIES! I DESIGNED ALL SORTS OF COSTUMES, AND PROPS! THEN, I GOT THE IDEA OF IMITATING YOU!"
SPIDERMAN
15

"I SPENT MANY LONG WEEKS STUDYING ALL YOUR POWERS, ALL YOUR ABILITIES--EVERYTHING THAT WAS KNOWN ABOUT YOU! I WAS SURE I COULD DUPLICATE YOUR FEATS!"
WHATEVER SPIDER-MAN DOES NATURALLY, I'LL FIND A WAY TO DO ARTIFICIALLY!
SENSES
WEB
JUMP CLING
TWO WAY MIRROR IDEA
CANNOT SEE IN--CAN SEE OUT
WEB--CANNOT DUPLICATE
"USING ALL THE SKILL I HAD AQUIRED DESIGNING MOVIE PROPS, I MADE A GUN WHICH FIRED A NYLO CORD RESEMBLING YOUR OWN WEB! I DESIGNED SHOES AND GLOVES WITH SPECIAL SUCTION CUPS, ENABLING ME TO CLING TO WALLS!"
MY SUCTION CUPS WORK! FROM A DISTANCE NO ONE WILL KNOW I'M NOT REALLY SPIDER-MAN!
"MY PLAN SEEMED PERFECT! I COULD COMMIT ALL SORTS OF CRIMES, AND YOU WOULD GET THE BLAME! BUT THEN I GOT A STILL GREATER IDEA! I WOULD CREATE A SEPARATE IDENTITY FOR MYSELF! I'D CALL MYSELF MYSTERIO! AND THEN I'D BATTLE YOU! WHEN I DEFEATED YOU, I'D BE A NATIONAL HERO--FOR NO ONE WOULD KNOW THAT MYSTERIO IS BOTH THE CRIMINAL AND THE CONQUEROR!"
"MY HELMET IS BASED ON THE PRINCIPLE OF YOUR EYE PIECES! I CAN SEE OUT, BUT NO ONE CAN SEE IN!"
"I CREATED A FINE SPRAY MADE OF SPECIALLY TREATED ACID WHICH WAS FOR THE SOLE PURPOSE OF DISSOLVING YOUR WEB IF YOU SHOULD EVER USE IT AGAINST ME!"
"THE BOTTOMS OF MY BOOTS CONTAIN CHEMICAL SMOKE EJECTORS AS WELL AS MAGNET PLATE SPRINGS WHICH ENABLE ME TO DUPLICATE YOUR OWN AMAZING LEAPS!"
EVEN MY NAME--MYSTERIO--WAS CREATED TO INSTIL AWE AND FEAR IN THE HEARTS OF MY ENEMIES!
I WAS ABLE TO SEE YOU WITHIN MY PROTECTIVE CLOUD BECAUSE I HAVE A BUILT IN SONAR DEVICE WHICH AIDS ME AT THE SAME TIME AS IT JAMS YOUR OWN SPIDER SENSE!
AND NOW, I SHALL DISPOSE OF YOU FOREVER!
DON'T COUNT ON IT, BIG MOUTH! I'VE GOT TO STAY AROUND LONG ENOUGH TO GIVE THIS TAPE RECORDER TO THE POLICE AND PROVE MY INNOCENCE!
A MINIATURE RECORDER!! BAH! IT WILL DO YOU NO GOOD! I'LL DESTROY IT--AFTER I'VE DEFEATED YOU!

BUT, IN A SPLIT-SECOND, SPIDER-MAN FLIPS BACKWARDS, OUT OF THE SPREADING MIST!
NOT THIS TIME, MYSTERIO! REMEMBER ONE THING-- YOUR POWER IS ARTIFICIAL -- BUT MINE IS NATURAL!!

AND I'LL BET ON MY NATURAL SPIDER POWERS ANY TIME!
I'VE GOT TO CIRCLE AROUND-- TRY TO FIND HIM WITHIN THE MIST!

HAVE TO KEEP MOVING FAST! CAN'T LOSE THE ADVANTAGE!
HE'S NOT HERE--OR HERE! BUT HE'S GOT TO BE NEARBY!

IF I KEEP SWINGING, THEN SOONER OR LATER I'LL--AHHH, I WAS RIGHT! THERE HE IS!
WHAM!

HEN, AS MYSTERIO OES SLIDING ALONG HE FLOOR INTO THE EXT-DOOR STUDIO...
OKAY, QUIET ON THE SET! LET'S ROLL 'EM! HUH? WAIT--WHAT'S THAT??
GET THAT GUY OUT OF HERE! HE'S IN THE WRONG MOVIE!

GANGWAY, BOYS!
I KNOW I'M NOT A MEMBER OF ACTORS' EQUITY, BUT I DON'T HAVE TIME TO GET A UNION CARD RIGHT NOW! I'VE GOT A LITTLE JOB TO FINISH FIRST!

YOU WON'T ESCAPE ME WITH THAT SMOKE CLOUD AGAIN! MY WEB WILL FALL OVER YOU LIKE A NET, TRAPPING YOU!
FOOL! I'M PREPARE
FOR ANYTHING YOU CA
DO!
YOU FORGET-- I USED TO BE A MOVIE STUNT MAN! I KNOW HOW TO ROLL WITH A PUNCH, SO AS NOT TO BE HURT!
AND NOW, I'LL USE MY SPECIAL SPRING BOOTS TO FRUSTRATE YOU AGAIN!

I'LL SIMPLY DISSOLVE YOUR WEB WITH MY CHEMICAL SPRAY AND-- OOOF!
THANKS, FELLA! I HOPED YOU'D DO THAT--TO GIVE ME A CHANCE TO WALLOP YOU!

THERE'S NOT A SPRING BUILT THAT'LL SAVE YOU FROM ME, MYSTERIO!!

NO! YOU CAN'T STOP ME! YOU CAN'T!! I'VE WAITED TOO LONG-- PLANNED TOO WELL!! I CAN'T BE THWARTED NOW!

ROLLING WITH THE PUNCH ISN'T GONNA HELP YOU NOW, MYSTERIO!

DIDN'T EXPECT ME TO LAND UPRIGHT DUE TO MY STUNT MAN TRAINING, DID YOU?
NOPE! I'M OVERWHELMED! I DON'T SEE HOW LITTLE UNTALENTED ME WILL EVER DEFEAT A GENIUS LIKE YOU!

SARCASM WON'T HELP YOU NOW! I STILL KNOW TRICKS YOU DON'T EVEN SUSPECT--LIKE TOSSING AN ENEMY OVER MY BACK THRU A SUDDEN MOVE!

AND NOW THAT YOU'RE OFF-BALANCE, I'LL-- HUH! WHERE'D HE GO??
UP HERE! I KNOW A TRICK OR TWO MYSELF!

YOU PICKED ON THE WRONG GUY WHEN YOU TRIED TO FRAME ME, MYSTERIO!
YOU SHOULDA FOUND SOME EASY VICTIM-- LIKE THE HUMAN TORCH, FOR INSTANCE!

DON'T JUST STAND THERE! SOMEBODY HELP MYSTERIO! SPIDER-MAN'S TURNED BAD!
SO YOU HELP MYSTERIO! I'M GETTIN' OUT OF HERE-- WHILE I STILL CAN!
19

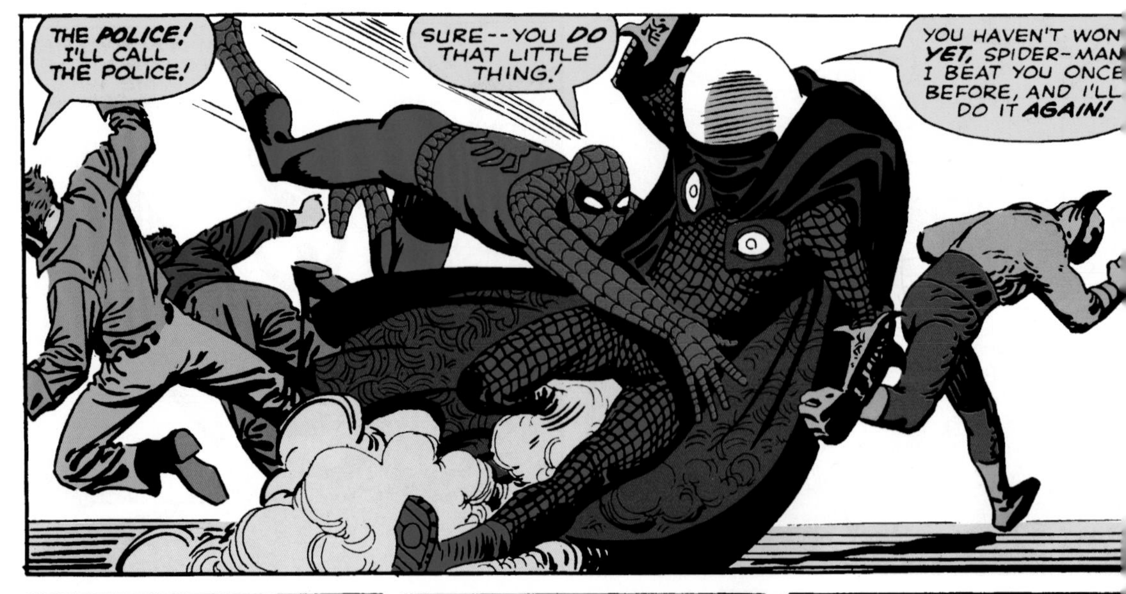
THE POLICE! I'LL CALL THE POLICE!
SURE--YOU DO THAT LITTLE THING!
YOU HAVEN'T WON YET, SPIDER-MAN! I BEAT YOU ONCE BEFORE, AND I'LL DO IT AGAIN!

USING YOUR LITTLE SMOKE ROUTINE AGAIN, EH?
I'LL SAY ONE THING FOR YOU, MYSTERIO--YOU NEVER LEARN!

YOUR CONCEALING SMOKE SCREEN WON'T HELP YOU WHILE I CAN USE MY SPIDER SENSE! AND YOU CAN'T STOP ME FROM USING IT IF I SMASH YOUR JAMMER--LIKE THIS!

AND NOW, I'LL DO YOU THE BEST FAVOR OF ALL--I'LL FINISH THIS OFF QUICKLY, SO THAT YOU WON'T GET TOO BORED!

I MUSTN'T FORGET TO TAKE MY AUTOMATIC CAMERA WHICH I HUNG ON A PIECE OF WEBBING UP HERE TO CATCH ALL THE ACTION!

I'LL FASTEN IT SECURELY TO MY BELT CONTAINER AGAIN! IT'S LIKE MONEY IN THE BANK TO ME!

AND NOW, ONE LAST PLUNGE INTO MYSTERIO'S CLOUD OF MIST, AND I'LL WRAP THIS THING UP FOR GOOD!

WITH MY SPIDER-SENSE COMPLETELY OPERATIONAL NOW, IT'S A BREEZE TO MAKE MY WAY THRU THE MIST AND LEAVE THE TV STUDIO UNSEEN BY ANYONE!

AND, WHEN THE STRANGE MIST FINALLY CLEARS...
FOR THE LUVVA PETE!! WHERE'D THEY GO??!
YOU NINCOMPOOP!! THE GREATEST ACTION SCENE IN HISTORY, AND YOU DIDN'T EVEN GET IT ON FILM!!!
B-BUT THEY WEREN'T MEMBERS OF THE CAST!! PROBABLY DIDN'T EVEN BELONG TO THE UNION!

ND, A FEW MINUTES LATER, AT POLICE HEADQUARTERS...
HEARD YSTERIO AS HERE! VH-WHAT APPENED, CHIEF??
IT'S INCREDIBLE, MR. JAMESON! SPIDER-MAN BROUGHT HIM IN, AND WE HAVE A FULL CONFES-SION ON TAPE FROM MYSTERIO'S OWN LIPS! HE'S THE CRIMINAL WE'VE BEEN SEEKING! SPIDER-MAN IS INNOCENT!!
OUR MEN ARE PICKING UP ALL THE STOLEN LOOT NOW, CHIEF-- THANKS TO SPIDER-MAN!

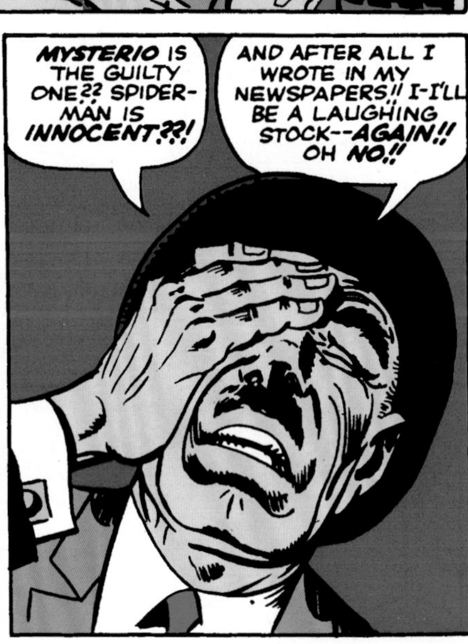
MYSTERIO IS THE GUILTY ONE?? SPIDER-MAN IS INNOCENT??!
AND AFTER ALL I WROTE IN MY NEWSPAPERS!! I-I'LL BE A LAUGHING STOCK--AGAIN!! OH NO!!

HEN, WHEN JAMESON RETURNS TO HIS OFFICE...
ANCEL ALL MY APPOINTMENTS, ISS BRANT! AND SEND DOWN OR A BOTTLE OF ASPIRIN-- A BIG BOTTLE!
ES SIR! PETER ARKER WAS UST IN! HE EFT SOME HOTOS FOR YOU!

HMMPH! A LOT OF GOOD PHOTOS CAN DO ME NOW! I'LL--HUH?? WHAT ARE THOSE?!!
FIGHT SCENES!! SPIDER-MAN AND MYSTERIO!!

THAT LUCKY PARKER!! HE MUST HAVE BEEN THERE JUST AT THE RIGHT TIME! THESE PICTURES ARE PERFECT FOR THE FRONT PAGE! I'M SAVED!
STOP THE PRESSES! WE'RE PUTTING OUT AN EXTRA!
21

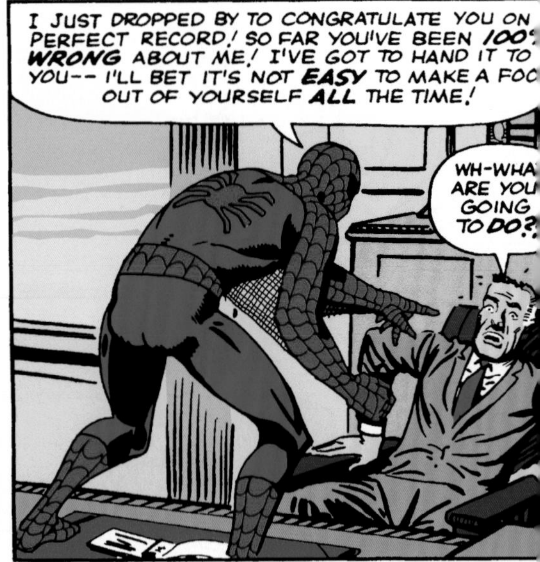

BUT, THAT DAY IS STILL IN THE FUTURE! AN UNTIL THEN, FATE HAS MANY MORE SURPRISE IN STORE FOR SPIDEY! NEXT ISSUE WE PRESENT ANOTHER BOOK-LENGTH ADVENTUR WITH AN UNEXPECTED GUEST STAR! WE THIN YOU'LL LIKE IT, SO--WE'LL SEE YOU THEN!

Amazing Spider-Man #618 Variant Cover by Joe Quinones

ART GALLERY

With his striking green and gold costume, audacious purple cloak and domed helmet, Mysterio is a villain whose appearance is always guaranteed to dominate any comic he appears in. Here we have just a small selection of artwork featuring the insane illusionist created by some of Marvel's top artists!

The Amazing Spider-Man #66
Cover Art by John Romita Sr.

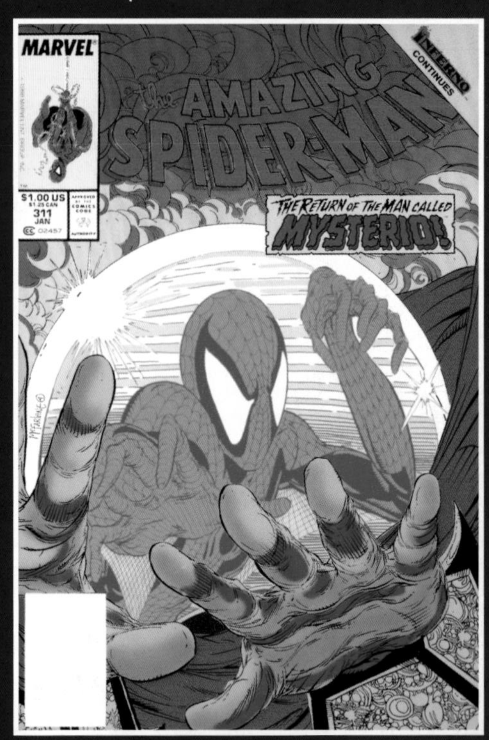

The Amazing Spider-Man #311
Cover Art by Todd McFarlane

Web-Spinners: Tales of Spider-Man #3
Cover Art by Vincent Locke

Internal art from *Daredevil Vol. 2 #6*
by Joe Quesada

Internal art from *Spider-Man Unlimited #7* by Gary Frank

Internal art from *Ben Reilly: Scarlet Spider #18* by Will Sliney

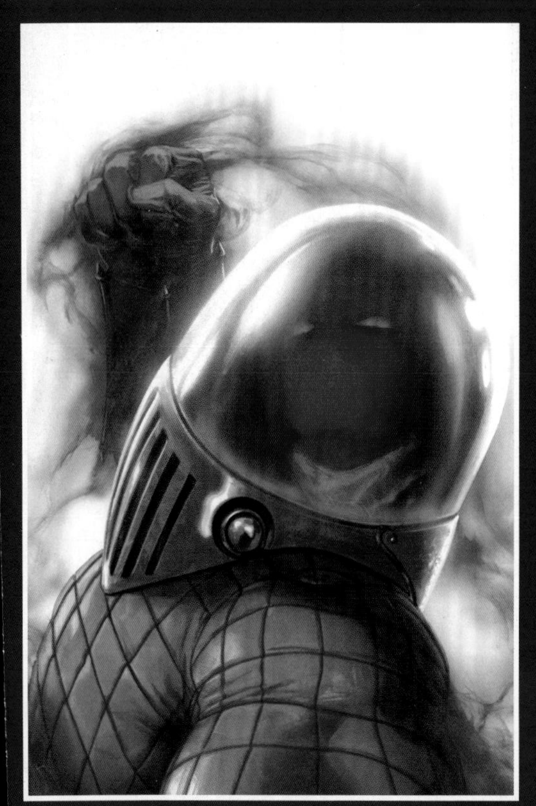

The Amazing Spider-Man #686 Variant Cover Art by Gabriele Dell'Otto

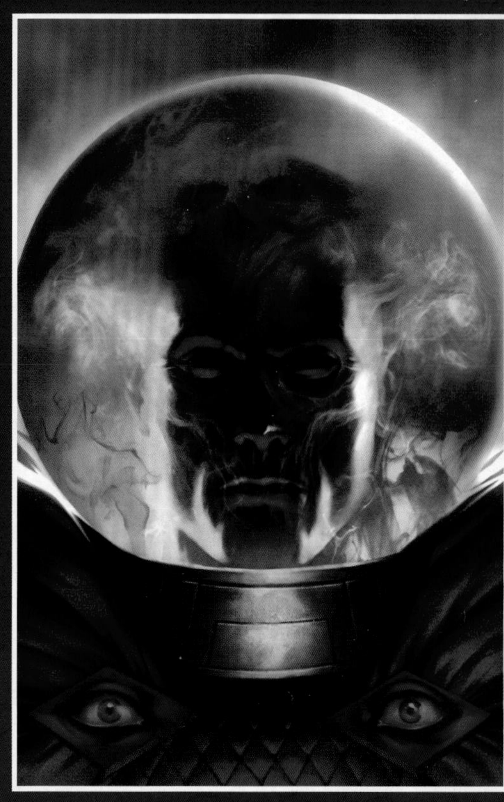

Web of Spider-Man Vol. 2 #4 Cover Art by Jelena Djurdjevic

EVEN MORE SPIDER-MAN ACTION!

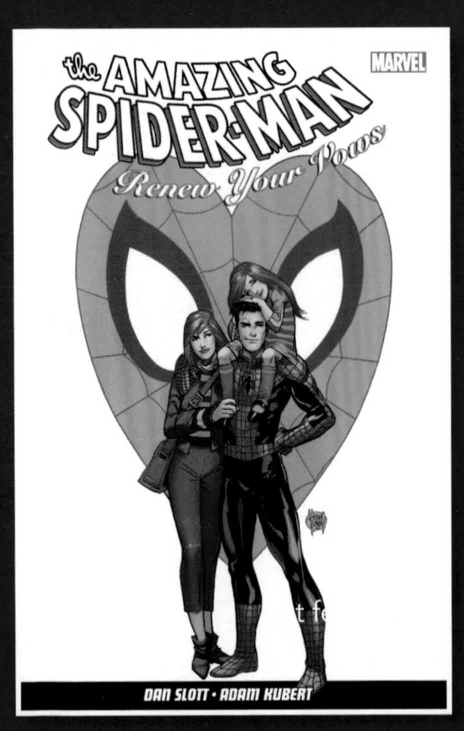

The Amazing Spider-Man: Renew Your Vows
ISBN: 9781846536922

The Amazing Spider-Man: Spider-Geddon
ISBN: 9781846539626

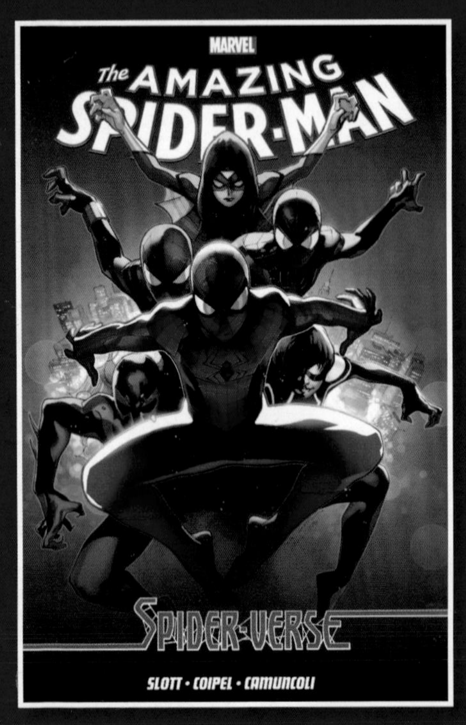

The Amazing Spider-Man: Spider-Verse
ISBN: 9781846536618

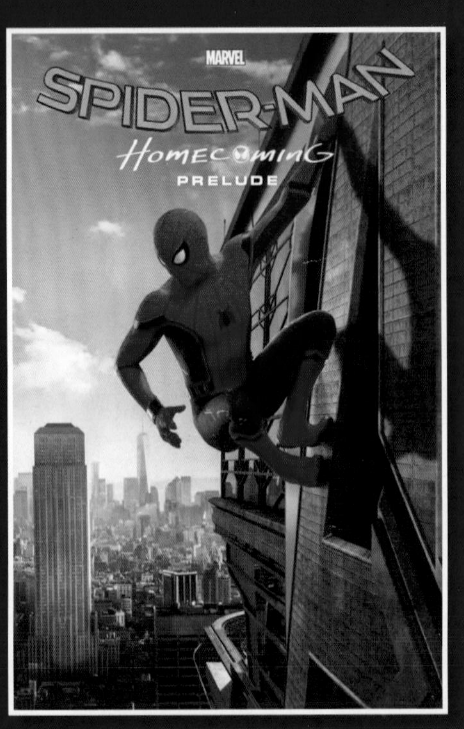

Marvel Cinematic Collection Vol. 1:
Spider-Man: Homecoming Prelude
ISBN: 9781846539930

Available now at all good book shops
or order online at store.panini.co.uk